AS Chemistry
UNIT 3

OCR

Module 2813: How Far, How Fast?
Experimental Skills 1

Mike Smith

Philip Allan Updates
Market Place
Deddington
Oxfordshire
OX15 0SE

tel: 01869 338652
fax: 01869 337590
e-mail: sales@philipallan.co.uk
www.philipallan.co.uk

© Philip Allan Updates 2002

ISBN 0 86003 690 1

This Guide has been written specifically to support students preparing for the OCR AS Chemistry Unit 3 examination. The content has been neither approved nor endorsed by OCR and remains the sole responsibility of the author.

Printed by Raithby, Lawrence & Co. Ltd, Leicester

Contents

Introduction

■ ■ ■

Content Guidance

■ ■ ■

Questions and Answers

Introduction

About this guide

This unit guide is the third in a series of three, which together cover the whole OCR AS Chemistry specification. This guide is written to help you to prepare for Unit Test 3, which examines the content of **Module 2813: How Far, How Fast?/Experimental Skills 1**. This is different from the previous two modules in that it is made up of more than one component:

- Component 01: How Far, How Fast?
- Component 02: Experimental Skills
- Component 03: Practical Examination

All candidates have to study Component 01, which is tested by a compulsory, written examination lasting 45 minutes. All candidates must also follow either Component 02 (practical assessments carried out in your own centre and marked by your teachers) *or* Component 03 (practical examination set by the examination board and marked by external examiners).

The majority of this guide is about Component 01 (How Far, How Fast?).

This **Introduction** provides advice on how to use the guide, together with suggestions for effective revision.

The **Content Guidance** section gives a point-by-point description of all the facts you need to know and concepts that you need to understand for Module 2813, Component 01. It aims to provide you with a basis for your revision. However, you must also be prepared to use other sources in your preparation for the examination. The remaining part of this section looks at Components 02 and 03. It includes some of the exemplar practical assessments provided by OCR.

The **Question and Answer** section shows you the sort of questions you can expect in the unit test. It would be impossible to give examples of every kind of question in one book, but the questions used should give you a flavour of what to expect. Each question has been attempted by two candidates, Candidate A and Candidate B. Their answers, along with the examiner's comments, should help you to see what you need to do to score a good mark — and how you can easily *not* score marks, even though you probably understand the chemistry.

What can I assume about the guide?

You can assume that:

- the topics covered in the Content Guidance section relate directly to those in the specification
- the basic facts you need to know are stated clearly

- the major concepts you need to understand are explained
- the questions at the end of the guide are similar in style to those that will appear in the unit test
- the answers supplied are genuine, combining responses commonly written by candidates
- the standard of the marking is broadly equivalent to the standard that will be applied to your answers

What can I *not* assume about the guide?

You must *not* assume that:
- every last detail has been covered
- the way in which the concepts are explained is the *only* way in which they can be presented in an examination (often concepts are presented in an unfamiliar situation)
- the range of question types presented is exhaustive (examiners are always thinking of new ways to test a topic)

So how should I use this guide?

The guide lends itself to a number of uses throughout your course — it is not *just* a revision aid.

The Content Guidance is laid out in sections that correspond to those of the specification for Module 2813 so that you can:
- use it to check that your notes cover the material required by the specification
- use it to identify strengths and weaknesses
- use it as a reference for homework and internal tests
- use it during your revision to prepare 'bite-sized' chunks of material rather than being faced with a file full of notes

The Question and Answer section can be used to:
- identify the terms used by examiners in questions and what they expect of you
- familiarise yourself with the style of questions you can expect
- identify the ways in which marks are lost or gained

Study skills and revision techniques

All students need to develop good study skills. This section provides advice and guidance on how to study AS chemistry.

Organising your notes

Chemistry students often accumulate a large quantity of notes, so it is useful to keep these in a well-ordered and logical manner. It is necessary to review your notes regularly, maybe rewriting the notes taken during lessons so that they are clear and concise, with key points highlighted. You should check your notes using textbooks and fill in any gaps. Make sure that you go back and ask your teacher if you are unsure about anything, especially if you find conflicting information in your class notes and textbook.

It is a good idea to file your notes in specification order using a consistent series of headings. The Content Guidance section can help you with this.

Organising your time

When organising your time, make sure that you plan carefully, allowing enough time to cover all of the work. It sounds easy, but it is one of the most difficult things to do. There is considerable evidence to show that revising for 2–3 hours at a time is counter-productive and that it is much better to work in short, sharp bursts of between 30 minutes and an hour.

Preparation for examinations is a very personal thing. Different people prepare, equally successfully, in very different ways. The key is being totally honest about what actually *works for you*.

Whatever your style, you must have a plan. Sitting down the night before the examination with a file full of notes and a textbook does not constitute a revision plan — it is just desperation — and you must not expect a great deal from it. Whatever your personal style, there are a number of things you *must* do and a number of other things you *could* do.

Component 01 is relatively brief, containing only three sections. The concepts introduced in this component are important and are built upon in Module 2816 in A2.

The scheme outlined below is a suggestion as to how you might revise Component 01 over a 3-week period. The work pattern shown is fairly simple. It involves revising and/or rewriting a topic and then over the next few days going through it repeatedly but never spending more than 30 minutes at a time. When you are confident that you have covered all areas, start trying to answer questions from past papers or this guide's Question and Answer section. Mark them yourself and seek help with anything that you are not sure about.

Day	Week 1	Week 2	Week 3
Mon	Topic 1 — Enthalpy changes (a) ΔH, exothermic and endothermic reactions, energy profile diagrams, standard enthalpy changes of formation and combustion Allow about 30 minutes	Reread all your summary notes at least twice	You have now revised all of Unit 3 and have attempted questions relating to each topic Make a list of your weaknesses and ask your teacher for help Reread all your summary notes at least twice Ask someone to test you

Day	Week 1	Week 2	Week 3
Tue	Topic 1 — Enthalpy changes (b) Bond enthalpy, $\Delta H = mc\Delta T$, Hess's law Allow about 30 minutes, followed by 10 minutes reading yesterday's notes on Topic 1(a)	Using past papers or other question sources, try a structured question on Topic 1 Mark it and list anything you do not understand Allow about 30 minutes	Using past papers or other question sources, try a relevant question that requires extended writing (essay-type questions) from any of the topics Mark it and list anything you do not understand Allow about 30 minutes
Wed	Topic 2 — Reaction rates (a) Qualitative explanation of the effect of concentration, temperature and catalysts on the rate of reaction; activation energy and Boltzmann distribution Allow about 30 minutes, followed by 10 minutes rereading yesterday's notes on Topic 1(b) and 5 minutes going over Topic 1(a)	Using past papers or other question sources, try a structured question on Topic 2 Mark it and list anything you do not understand Allow about 30 minutes	Using past papers or other question sources, try a relevant question that requires extended writing (essay-type questions) from any of the topics Mark it and list anything you do not understand Allow about 30 minutes
Thu	Topic 2 — Reaction rates (b) Catalysts Allow about 30 minutes, followed by 10 minutes rereading yesterday's notes on Topic 2(a), 5 minutes going over Topic 1(b) and, finally, 2 minutes on Topic 1(a)	Using past papers or other question sources, try a structured question on Topic 3 Mark it and list anything you do not understand Allow about 30 minutes	Collect together about four structured questions and one extended answer question covering all three topics and try them under exam conditions Allow 45 minutes Mark them and list anything you do not understand
Fri	Topic 3 — Chemical equilibrium (a) Le Chatelier's principle and the Haber process Allow about 30 minutes, followed by 10 minutes rereading yesterday's notes on Topic 2(b), 5 minutes going over Topic 2(a) and, finally, 2 minutes on Topics 1(a) and 1(b)	Using past papers or other question sources, try a structured question on each of the three topics Mark them and list anything you do not understand Allow about 30 minutes	Reread all your summary notes at least twice Concentrate on the weaknesses you identified on Monday (by now you should have talked to your teacher about them) Ask someone to test you

Day	Week 1	Week 2	Week 3
Sat	Topic 3 — Chemical equlibrium (b) Acids and bases Allow about 30 minutes, followed by 10 minutes rereading yesterday's notes on Topic 3(a), 5 minutes going over Topics 2(a) and 2(b) and, finally, 1 minute on Topics 1(a) and 1(b)	Rest	Rest
Sun	General revision of all three topics Allow about 30 minutes in total Topic 3 — 15 minutes Topic 2 — 10 minutes Topic 1 — 5 minutes	Using past papers or other question sources, try a structured question on each of the three topics Mark them and list anything you do not understand Allow about 30 minutes	Attempt a past exam paper Allow 45 minutes Use your notes and other sources to mark your responses List anything you do not understand Plan to see your teacher for additional help with your weaknesses

This revision timetable may not suit you, in which case write one to meet your needs. It is only there to give you an idea of how one might work. The most important thing is that the grid at least enables you to see what you should be doing and when you should be doing it. Do not try to be too ambitious — *little and often is by far the best way*.

It would of course be sensible to put together a longer rolling programme to cover all your AS subjects. Do *not* leave it too late. Start sooner rather than later.

Things you *must* do

- Leave yourself enough time to cover *all* the material.
- Make sure that you actually *have* all the material to hand (use this book as a basis).
- Identify weaknesses early in your preparation so that you have time to do something about them.
- Familiarise yourself with the terminology used in examination questions.

Things you *could* do to help you learn

- Copy selected portions of your notes.
- Write a precis of your notes, which includes all the key points.
- Write key points on postcards (carry them round with you for a quick revise during a coffee break!).

- Discuss a topic with a friend also studying the same course.
- Try to explain a topic to someone *not* on the course.
- Practise examination questions on the topic.

Approaching the unit test

Terms used in the unit test

You will be asked precise questions in the unit test, so you can save a lot of valuable time as well as ensuring you score as many marks as possible by knowing what is expected. Terms used most commonly are explained below.

Define
This requires a precise statement to explain a chemical term. It could involve specific amounts or conditions such as temperature and pressure.

Explain
This normally implies that a definition should be given, together with some relevant comment on the significance or context of the term(s) concerned, especially where two or more terms are included in the question. The amount of supplementary comment should be determined by the mark allocation.

State
This implies a concise answer with little or no supporting argument.

Describe
This requires you to state in words (but using diagrams where appropriate) the main points of the topic. It is often used with reference either to particular phenomena or to particular experiments. In the former instance, the term usually implies that the answer should include reference to observations associated with the phenomena. The amount of description should be determined by the mark allocation. You are not expected to explain the phenomena or experiments, but merely to describe them.

Deduce or predict
This means that you are not expected to produce the answer by recall but by making a logical connection between other pieces of information. Such information may be wholly given in the question or could depend on answers given in an earlier part of the question. 'Predict' also implies a concise answer, with no supporting statement required.

Outline
This implies brevity, i.e. restricting the answer to essential detail only.

Suggest
This is used in two contexts. It implies either that there is no unique answer or that you are expected to apply your knowledge to a 'novel' situation that may not be formally in the specification.

Calculate

This is used when a numerical answer is required. In general, working should be shown.

Sketch

When this is applied to diagrams, it means that a simple, freehand drawing is acceptable. Nevertheless, care should be taken over proportions, and important details should be labelled clearly.

On the day

When you finally open the test paper, it can be quite a stressful moment and you need to be certain of your strategy. The test paper consists of structured questions (usually three or four) and free-response questions (usually one). The structured questions usually account for between 30 and 35 marks and the free-response questions are worth 10 to 15 marks. The total number of marks on the paper is 45.

Time will be very tight; there are only 45 minutes for this 45-mark paper. So:
- do *not* begin writing as soon as you open the paper
- scan *all* the questions before you begin to answer any
- identify those questions about which you feel most confident
- *read the question carefully* — if you are asked to explain, then explain, do *not* just describe
- take notice of the mark allocation and do not supply the examiner with all your knowledge of any topic if there is only 1 mark allocated — similarly, you have to come up with *four* ideas if 4 marks are allocated
- try to stick to the point in your answer — it is easy to stray into related areas that will not score marks and will use up valuable time
- try to answer *all* the questions

Structured questions

These are questions that may require a single-word answer, a short sentence or a response amounting to several sentences. The setter for the paper will have thought carefully about the amount of space required for the answer and the marks allocated, so the space provided usually gives a good indication of the amount of detail required.

Free-response questions

These questions enable you to demonstrate the depth and breadth of your knowledge as well as your ability to communicate chemical ideas in a concise way. These questions will often include marks for the quality of written communication. You are expected to use appropriate scientific terminology and to write in continuous prose, paying particular attention to spelling, punctuation and grammar.

Content
Guidance

This Content Guidance section is a student's guide to Module 2813.

The main topics are:
- Enthalpy changes
- Reaction rates
- Chemical equilibrium

This section includes all the relevant key facts required by the specification and explains the essential concepts.

At the end of this Content Guidance section there is advice on the practical skills required by Components 02 and 03 followed by information on how these are assessed.

Enthalpy changes

Enthalpy changes: ΔH of reaction, formation, combustion

Enthalpy change is the exchange of energy between a reaction mixture and its surroundings. The enthalpy change is measured at constant temperature and constant pressure and is given the symbol ΔH. The units are $kJ\,mol^{-1}$.

The symbol Δ is often used in chemistry. It indicates a change in a parameter:
- ΔT = change in temperature
- ΔV = change in volume
- ΔP = change in pressure

If the reaction mixture loses energy to its surroundings, the reaction is exothermic and ΔH is negative.

If the reaction mixture gains energy from its surroundings, the reaction is endothermic and ΔH is positive.

ΔH can be calculated using the following equation:

ΔH = enthalpy of products – enthalpy of reactants

Enthalpy changes can be represented by simple enthalpy profile diagrams.

For an **exothermic reaction**, the enthalpy profile diagram shows the products at a lower energy than the reactants. The difference in the enthalpy is ΔH.

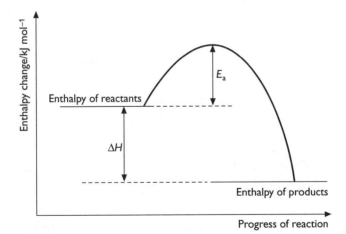

For an **endothermic reaction**, the enthalpy profile diagram shows the products at a higher energy than the reactants. The difference in the enthalpy is ΔH.

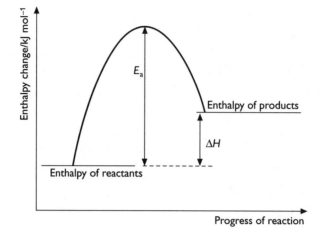

Combustion reactions are usually exothermic, releasing energy to the surroundings. This results in an increase in temperature of the surroundings. The enthalpy profile below illustrates the combustion of methane.

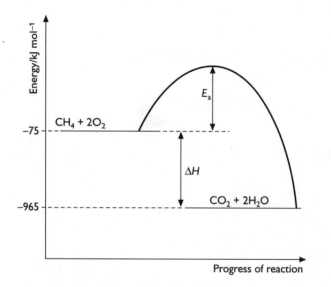

The **enthalpy of combustion** of methane is calculated using the equation:

ΔH = enthalpy of products − enthalpy of reactants

$= (-965) - (-75) = -965 + 75 = -890\,\mathrm{kJ\,mol^{-1}}$

Thermal decomposition reactions are usually endothermic, requiring energy from the surroundings. The enthalpy profile for the thermal decomposition of calcium carbonate is shown below.

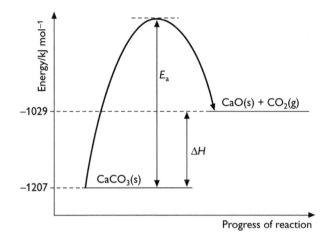

The **thermal decomposition** of calcium carbonate is calculated using the equation:

ΔH = enthalpy of products – enthalpy of reactants

$= (-1029) - (-1207) = -1029 + 1207 = +178 \text{ kJ mol}^{-1}$

Enthalpy profile diagrams not only show the enthalpy change of reaction, ΔH, but also display the activation energy, E_a.

Activation energy is the minimum energy needed for colliding particles to react. (This is covered in more detail in the section on reaction rates, page 27.) In any chemical reaction, bonds are broken and new bonds are formed. Breaking a bond is an endothermic process requiring energy. This energy requirement contributes to the activation energy of the reaction.

Ammonia, NH_3, can be formed by the reaction between nitrogen and hydrogen. (This is covered in more detail on page 34.) The reaction is reversible. The enthalpy of reaction is the same for the forward and the reverse reactions, but the activation energy is different.

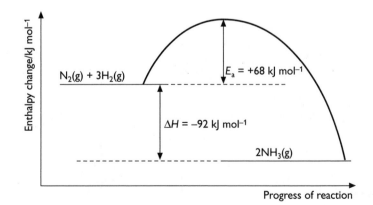

Activation energy for the forward reaction is +68 kJ mol^{-1}. For the reverse reaction, the activation energy is +(68 + 92) = +160 kJ mol^{-1}.

For each of the reactions below, the bonds broken and formed are shown.

Combustion of hydrogen:

$$2H_2 + O_2 \longrightarrow 2H_2O$$

Bond broken	Number	Bond formed	Number
H–H	2	O–H	4
O=O	1		

Combustion of methane:

$$CH_4 + 2O_2 \longrightarrow CO_2 + 2H_2O$$

It is useful to draw out the reaction, using displayed formulae so that all the bonds broken and formed can be seen clearly.

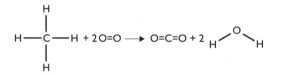

Bond broken	Number	Bond formed	Number
C–H	4	C=O	2
O=O	2	O–H	4

Combustion of propane:

$$C_3H_8 + 5O_2 \longrightarrow 3CO_2 + 4H_2O$$

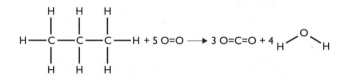

Bond broken	Number	Bond formed	Number
C–H	8	C=O	6
C–C	2	O–H	8
O=O	5		

The three exothermic reactions above are all oxidation reactions. Each gives out energy to the surroundings and therefore is exothermic. The energy released by the formation of bonds in the products exceeds the energy used in breaking the bonds in the reactants.

Standard enthalpy changes

All standard enthalpy changes are measured under **standard conditions**. The temperature and the pressure at which measurements and calculations are carried out are standardised.

- Standard temperature = 298 K (25 °C)
- Standard pressure = 100 kPa (100 000 N m^{-2} = 10^5 Pa = 1 bar = 1 atm)
- Standard temperature and pressure are often referred to as s.t.p.

Examinations often ask for definitions of enthalpy changes and it is advisable to learn these.

- **Standard enthalpy change of formation** is the enthalpy change when 1 mole of a substance is formed from its elements, in their natural state, under standard conditions of 298 K and 100 kPa.
- **Standard enthalpy change of combustion** is the enthalpy change when 1 mole of a substance is burnt completely, in an excess of oxygen, under standard conditions of 298 K and 100 kPa.
- **Average bond enthalpy** is the enthalpy change on breaking one mole of a covalent bond in a gaseous molecule under standard conditions of 298 K and 100 kPa.

You may also have to show your understanding by writing equations illustrating the standard enthalpy changes of formation and of combustion.

Standard enthalpy of formation equations

- **Ethane, C_2H_6:**

1 mole of product must always be formed even if it means using fractions in the balanced equation — see equation (iii)

$$2C(s) + 3H_2(g) \longrightarrow 1C_2H_6(g)$$

It is essential to show all state symbols

- **Ethanoic acid, CH_3CO_2H:**

$$2C(s) + 2H_2(g) + O_2(g) \longrightarrow 1CH_3CO_2H(l)$$

- **Ethanamide, CH_3CONH_2:**

$$2C(s) + 2\tfrac{1}{2}H_2(g) + \tfrac{1}{2}O_2(g) + \tfrac{1}{2}N_2(g) \longrightarrow 1CH_3CONH_2(s)$$

Standard enthalpy of combustion equations

- **Ethane, C_2H_6:**

1 mole of reactant must always be used even if it means using fractions in the balanced equation

$$1\ C_2H_6(g) + 3\tfrac{1}{2}\,O_2(g) \longrightarrow 2CO_2(g) + 3H_2O(l)$$

It is essential to show all state symbols

- **Ethanoic acid, CH_3CO_2H:**

$$1CH_3CO_2H(l) + 2O_2(g) \longrightarrow 2CO_2(g) + 2H_2O(l)$$

- **Ethanol, CH_3CH_2OH:**

$$1CH_3CH_2OH(l) + 3O_2(g) \longrightarrow 2CO_2(g) + 3H_2O(l)$$

Bond enthalpy

Bond (dissociation) enthalpy is energy needed to break bonds. It is always endothermic $(+\Delta H)$. The breaking of a bond, by homolytic fission (see the guide to Module 2812), produces two uncharged particles:

$$H–Cl(g) \longrightarrow H(g) + Cl(g)$$

Where a molecule contains more than one bond of the same type, the bond enthalpy is the average (mean) value. In water, for instance, the chemical environment is changed once the first bond has been broken, resulting in a different bond enthalpy for the two bonds.

$$H{-}O{-}H\,(g) \longrightarrow H{-}O\,(g) + H(g) \qquad \Delta H = +496\ kJ\ mol^{-1}$$

$$H{-}O\,(g) \longrightarrow H(g) + O(g) \qquad \Delta H = +432\ kJ\ mol^{-1}$$

O–H bond enthalpy in water is quoted as $+\dfrac{(496 + 432)}{2} = +464\ kJ\ mol^{-1}$.

Measuring enthalpy changes

For many reactions, enthalpy change can be measured directly, using the simple apparatus shown below.

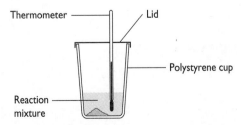

Thermometer — Lid

Polystyrene cup

Reaction mixture

The enthalpy change for the reaction mixture can be calculated by using the equation:
$$\Delta H = -mc\Delta T$$

- m = mass of the reaction mixture
- c = the specific heat capacity of the reaction mixture
- ΔT = the change in temperature

The solvent for many reactions is water. The specific heat capacity of water is $4.2\,J\,g^{-1}K^{-1}$ (or $4.2\,kJ\,kg^{-1}K^{-1}$).

The enthalpy change for the reaction mixture will have a ΔH value in either joules (J) or kilojoules (kJ), depending on the specific heat capacity units. It is usual to quote ΔH for one mole of reactant with the units in $kJ\,mol^{-1}$. This may require mole calculations (see the guide to Module 2811).

Hess's law and enthalpy cycles

For energetic or kinetic reasons, the enthalpy changes of many chemical reactions cannot be measured experimentally, but they can be calculated using Hess's law. If the activation energy is very high, it is unlikely that the reaction will take place under standard conditions — therefore, measurements cannot be made. The reaction may be too slow under standard conditions for measurements to be made.

Hess's law states that the enthalpy change for a reaction is the same irrespective of the route taken, provided that the initial and final conditions are the same. It is often useful to construct an enthalpy triangle, as shown below.

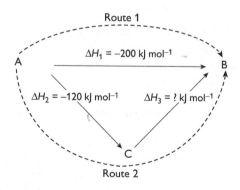

Hess's law tells us that the enthalpy change for route 1 is equal to the enthalpy change for route 2:
$$\Delta H_1 = \Delta H_2 + \Delta H_3$$

Therefore,
$$\begin{aligned}\Delta H_3 &= \Delta H_1 - \Delta H_2 \\ &= (-200) - (-120) \\ &= -200 + 120 \\ &= -80\,kJ\,mol^{-1}\end{aligned}$$

Hess's law can be used to calculate enthalpy changes.

Enthalpy change of formation from enthalpy changes of combustion

- Write an equation for the enthalpy of formation required.
- Construct the enthalpy triangle by writing the combustion products at the bottom.
- Both arrows point downwards.

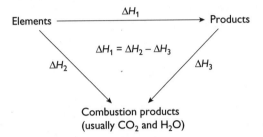

Enthalpy change of combustion from enthalpy changes of formation

- Write an equation for the enthalpy of combustion required.
- Construct the enthalpy triangle by writing the elements at the bottom.
- Both arrows point upwards.

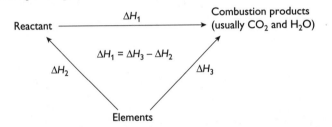

Enthalpy change of formation from enthalpy changes of combustion

Calculate the standard enthalpy of formation of methane and ethanol by:

- constructing a suitable Hess's cycle
- using the data in the table below

Name	Formula	$\Delta H_c^{\ominus}$/kJ mol^{-1}
Graphite (carbon)	C	−393.5
Hydrogen	H_2	−285.8
Methane	CH_4	−890.3
Ethanol	C_2H_5OH	−1367.3

- **Methane**

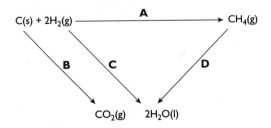

Applying Hess's law to the enthalpy triangle:

A = **B** + **C** – **D**

B = enthalpy of combustion of $C(s)$ = $-393.5\,kJ\,mol^{-1}$

C = $2 \times$ (enthalpy of combustion of $H_2(g)$)

= $2 \times (-285.8)$ = $-571.6\,kJ\,mol^{-1}$

D = enthalpy of combustion of $CH_4(g)$ = $-890.3\,kJ\,mol^{-1}$

A = **B** + **C** – **D**

= $(-393.5) + (-571.6) - (-890.3)$

= $-965.1 + 890.3 = -74.8\,kJ\,mol^{-1}$

The standard enthalpy of formation of methane is $-74.8\,kJ\,mol^{-1}$.

- **Ethanol**

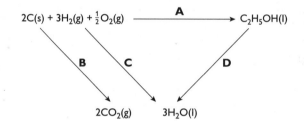

Applying Hess's law to the enthalpy triangle:

A = **B** + **C** – **D**

B = $2 \times$ (enthalpy of combustion of $C(s)$) = $2 \times (-393.5)$ = $-787.0\,kJ\,mol^{-1}$

C = $3 \times$ (enthalpy of combustion of $H_2(g)$) = $3 \times (-285.8)$ = $-857.4\,kJ\,mol^{-1}$

D = enthalpy of combustion of $C_2H_5OH(l)$ = $-1367.3\,kJ\,mol^{-1}$

A = **B** + **C** – **D**

= $(-787.0) + (-857.4) - (-1367.3)$

= $-1644.4 + 1367.3 = -277.1\,kJ\,mol^{-1}$

The standard enthalpy of formation of ethanol is $-277.1\,kJ\,mol^{-1}$.

Enthalpy change of combustion from enthalpy changes of formation

Calculate the standard enthalpy of combustion of ethane and methanol by:

- constructing a suitable Hess's cycle
- using the data in the table below

Name	Formula	$\Delta H_f^{\ominus}/kJ\,mol^{-1}$
Carbon dioxide	CO_2	-393.5
Water	H_2O	-285.8
Ethane	C_2H_6	-84.7
Methanol	CH_3OH	-239.1

- **Ethane**

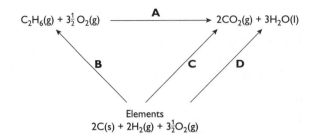

Applying Hess's law to the enthalpy triangle:

A = C + D − B
C = 2 × (enthalpy of formation of $CO_2(g)$) = 2 × (−393.5) = −787.0 kJ mol^{-1}
D = 3 × (enthalpy of formation of $H_2O(l)$) = 3 × (−285.8) = −857.4 kJ mol^{-1}
B = enthalpy of formation of $C_2H_6(g)$ = −84.7 kJ mol^{-1}

A = C + D − B
A = (−787.0) + (−857.4) − (−84.7)
= −1644.4 + 84.7
= −1559.7 kJ mol^{-1}

The standard enthalpy of combustion of ethane is −1559.7 kJ mol^{-1}.

- **Methanol**

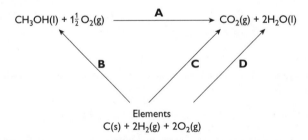

Applying Hess's law to the enthalpy triangle:

A = C + D − B
C = enthalpy of formation of $CO_2(g)$
= −393.5 kJ mol^{-1}
D = 2 × (enthalpy of formation of $H_2O(l)$) = 2 × (−285.8) = −571.6 kJ mol^{-1}
B = enthalpy of formation of $CH_3OH(g)$ = −239.1 kJ mol^{-1}

A = C + D − B
A = (−393.5) + (−571.6) − (−239.1)
= −965.1 + 239.1
= −726.0 kJ mol^{-1}

The standard enthalpy of combustion of ethane is −726.0 kJ mol^{-1}.

Hess's law calculations

Hess's law can also be used to calculate the enthalpy change for a reaction, ΔH_r.
Calculate ΔH_r for:

$$2CO(g) + O_2(g) \longrightarrow 2CO_2(g)$$

The standard enthalpies of formation of $CO(g)$ and $CO_2(g)$ are -110 and $-394\,kJ\,mol^{-1}$ respectively.

Step 1: Write the equation for whatever you have been asked to calculate.

$$2CO(g) + O_2(g) \xrightarrow{\Delta H_R} 2CO_2(g)$$

Step 2: Link both sides of the equation to the data given.

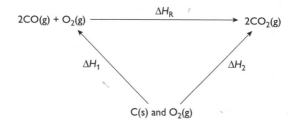

Step 3: Apply Hess' Law, $\Delta H_R = \Delta H_2 - \Delta H_1$

$\Delta H_1 = 2 \times (-110) = -220$

$\Delta H_2 = -394$

$\Delta H_R = -394 - (-220)$

$\quad\quad = -394 + 220$

$\quad\quad = -174\,kJ\,mol^{-1}$

Enthalpy of reaction from bond enthalpies

Calculate the enthalpy change of combustion for propane and ethanol using the table of bond enthalpy data.

Formula	$\Delta H/kJ\,mol^{-1}$
C=O	+805
C–H	+413
C–O	+358
O=O	+498
O–H	+464
C–C	+347

- **Propane**

$$C_3H_8(g) + 5O_2(g) \longrightarrow 3CO_2(g) + 4H_2O(l)$$

It is always helpful to draw out the displayed formulae of the reagents and products.

$$H-C-C-C-H + 5\,O{=}O \longrightarrow 3\,O{=}C{=}O + 4\,H{-}O{-}H$$

Bonds broken	Total enthalpy change
$2 \times$ C–C	+694
$8 \times$ C–H	+3304
$5 \times$ O=O	+2490

Energy required to break all bonds = $+6488\,\text{kJ}\,\text{mol}^{-1}$

Bonds formed	Total enthalpy change
$6 \times$ C=O	−4830
$8 \times$ O–H	−3712

Energy released by formation of all bonds = $-8542\,\text{kJ}\,\text{mol}^{-1}$

Bond enthalpy change = $+6488 - 8542 = -2054\,\text{kJ}\,\text{mol}^{-1}$

This is the enthalpy of combustion of ethanol.

- **Ethanol**

$$C_2H_5OH(g) + 3O_2(g) \longrightarrow 2CO_2(g) + 3H_2O(l)$$

It is always helpful to draw out the displayed formulae of the reagents and products.

$$H-C-C-O-H + 3\,O{=}O \longrightarrow 2\,O{=}C{=}O + 3\,H{-}O{-}H$$

Bonds broken	Total enthalpy change
C–C	+347
$5 \times$ C–H	+2065
C–O	+358
O–H	+464
$3 \times$ O=O	+1494

Energy required to break all bonds = +4728 kJ mol^{-1}

Bonds formed	Total enthalpy change
4 × C=O	−3220
6 × O–H	−2784

Energy released by formation of all bonds = −6004 kJ mol^{-1}

Bond enthalpy change = +4728 − 6004 = −1276 kJ mol^{-1}

This is the enthalpy of combustion of ethanol.

Calculations using $\Delta H = -mc\Delta T$

Enthalpy of neutralisation

25 cm^3 of 1.0 mol dm^{-3} HCl(aq) were added to 25 cm^3 of 1.0 mol dm^{-3} NaOH(aq) in a polystyrene cup. The temperature rose by 6.9 °C. Calculate the enthalpy change of neutralisation for HCl(aq). (Specific heat capacity, $c = 4.2$ J g^{-1}K^{-1}; the density of the reaction mixture = 1.0 g cm^{-3}.)

ΔH for the reaction is calculated by using the equation $\Delta H = -mc\Delta T$

Volume of the reaction mixture = 25 cm^3 + 25 cm^3 = 50 cm^3

Density of the reaction mixture = 1.0 g cm^{-3}

Therefore, the mass of the reaction mixture = 50 g

$$m = 50\,g$$
$$c = 4.2\,J\,g^{-1}K^{-1}$$
$$\Delta T = 6.9\,K$$
$$\Delta H = -mc\Delta T$$
$$= -(50 \times 4.2 \times 6.9)$$
$$= -1449\,J = -1.449\,kJ$$

Note the units are in kJ and *not* in kJ mol^{-1}.

The value calculated relates to the neutralisation of 25 cm^3 of 1.0 mol dm^{-3} HCl, which is equivalent to 0.025 moles. (See the guide to Module 2811.)

$$n = cV = 1.0 \times 25/1000 = 0.025 \text{ moles}$$

The ΔH value for the reaction is −1.449 kJ per 0.025 mol of HCl(aq). This can be converted to kJ mol^{-1} by dividing both numbers by 0.025.

$$\Delta H = \frac{-1.449}{0.025}\,kJ \text{ per } \frac{0.025}{0.025}\,mol$$
$$= -57.96\,kJ \text{ per } 1.0\,mol$$
$$= -58\,kJ\,mol^{-1}$$

(The answer is quoted to 2 significant figures in line with the measurements, which were also given to 2 significant figures.)

Enthalpy of combustion of ethanol

The enthalpy of combustion of ethanol was measured using the apparatus shown below.

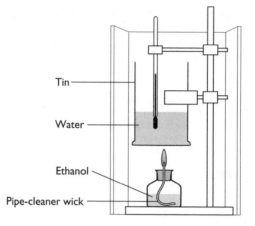

Tin

Water

Ethanol

Pipe-cleaner wick

100 cm³ water was placed in a beaker and the initial temperature taken. A bottle containing ethanol, a wick and a bung were weighed and placed in position, as shown in the diagram. The wick was lit and the ethanol burnt. The temperature of the water was monitored and the ethanol was allowed to burn for 5 minutes. The flame was extinguished and the final temperature of the water measured. The bottle containing the ethanol was reweighed.

Results:
- Initial temperature = 24.2 °C
- Final temperature = 38.5 °C
- Rise in temperature = 14.3 °C
- Initial mass of bottle + ethanol = 145.65 g
- Final mass of bottle + ethanol = 145.42 g
- Mass of ethanol used = 0.23 g

Calculation:

Specific heat capacity, $c = 4.2\,\mathrm{J\,g^{-1}K^{-1}}$; the density of water = $1.0\,\mathrm{g\,cm^{-3}}$

ΔH for the reaction is calculated by using the equation $\Delta H = -mc\Delta T$

Volume of water = 100 cm³

Density of water = $1.0\,\mathrm{g\,cm^{-3}}$

Therefore, the mass of water = 100 g

$$m = 100\,\mathrm{g}$$
$$c = 4.2\,\mathrm{J\,g^{-1}K^{-1}}$$
$$\Delta T = 14.3\,\mathrm{K}$$
$$\Delta H = -mc\Delta T$$
$$= -(100 \times 4.2 \times 14.3)$$
$$= -6006\,\mathrm{J} = -6.006\,\mathrm{kJ}$$

Note the units are in kJ and *not* in kJ mol^{-1}.

The value calculated relates to the combustion of 0.23 g of ethanol, which is equivalent to 0.005 moles ($n = m/M_r = 0.23/46$). (See the guide to Module 2811.)

The ΔH value for the reaction is -6.006 kJ per 0.005 mol of ethanol. This can be converted to kJ mol^{-1} by dividing both numbers by 0.005.

$$\Delta H = \frac{-6.006}{0.005} \text{ kJ per } \frac{-0.005}{0.005} \text{ mol}$$
$$= -1201.2 \text{ kJ per } 1.0 \text{ mol}$$
$$= -1201.2 \text{ kJ mol}^{-1}$$

Reaction rates

Experimental observations show that the rate of a reaction is influenced by temperature, concentration, pressure and the use of a catalyst.

Collision theory

The collision theory of reactivity helps to provide explanations for these observations. A reaction cannot take place unless a collision occurs between reacting particles. Increasing the temperature or concentration increases the chance of a collision occurring.

However, not all collisions lead to a successful reaction. The energy of a collision between reacting particles must exceed the minimum energy required for the reaction to occur. This minimum energy is known as the activation energy, E_a. Increasing the temperature affects the number of collisions, with energy exceeding the activation energy. Catalysts reduce the activation energy.

Energy is directly proportional to absolute temperature. Particles involved in a collision exchange (gain or lose) energy, even if a reaction does not occur. It follows that for any given mass of gaseous reactants at constant temperature, there will be a distribution of energies, with some particles having more energy than others.

Boltzmann distribution of molecular energies

The graph below shows a typical distribution of energies at constant temperature.

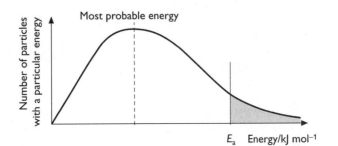

- The distribution always goes through the origin because there are no particles with zero energy.
- The distribution is asymptotic to the horizontal axis at high energy, indicating there is no maximum energy. (Asymptotic means that the curve approaches the axis but will only meet it at infinity.)
- E_a represents the activation energy — the minimum energy required to start the reaction.
- The area under the curve is proportional to the total number of particles.
- The shaded area represents the particles with sufficient energy to react. These are the particles with energy greater than or equal to the activation energy ($E \geq E_a$).

Effect of concentration on the rate of reaction

A useful analogy is to imagine your first driving lesson. The one thing you want to avoid is a collision! It follows that your first lesson is likely to be early on Sunday morning on a quiet country lane, rather than at 5.00 p.m. on a Friday evening in the city centre. It is obvious that the high concentration of cars at rush hour increases the chance of a collision. The same is true for a chemical reaction. Increasing concentration simply increases the chance of a collision. The more collisions there are, the faster the reaction will be.

Effect of pressure on the rate of reaction

For a gaseous reaction, increasing pressure has the same effect as increasing concentration. At constant temperature, an increase in pressure results in a decrease in volume (PV = constant). As the volume decreases, the concentration increases. Gases, therefore, react faster at high pressure because there is an increased chance of a collision.

Effect of temperature on the rate of reaction

An increase in temperature has a dramatic effect on the distribution of energies, as can be seen in the graph below.

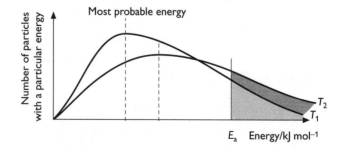

Only the temperature has changed. The number of particles is constant, so the area under both curves remains the same.

content guidance

At higher temperature, T_2, the distribution flattens and shifts to the right because:
- there are fewer particles with low energy
- the most probable energy moves to higher energy
- a greater proportion of particles have energy exceeding the activation energy

Raising the temperature increases the number of particles with energy greater than or equal to the activation energy ($E \geq E_a$) which means that at high temperature, there are more particles with sufficient energy to react. Therefore, the reaction is faster.

Effect of catalysts on the rate of reaction

From GCSE you will recall that catalysts speed up reactions without themselves being changed permanently.

Catalysts are subdivided into two types: **homogeneous** and **heterogeneous** (see page 30). Both types work by lowering the activation energy for the reaction. This is illustrated below on an energy profile diagram.

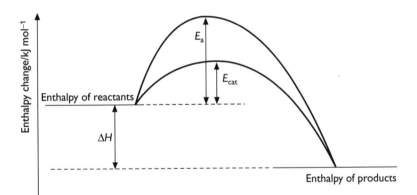

- E_a is the activation energy of the uncatalysed reaction.
- E_{cat} is the activation energy of the catalysed reaction.

A catalyst lowers the activation energy, but does not alter the Boltzmann distribution. It changes the number of particles with energy greater than or equal to the new activation energy, E_{cat}.

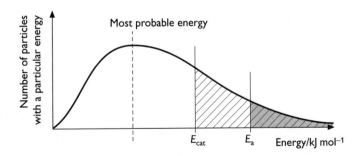

The shaded areas indicate the proportion of particles with energy exceeding the activation energies.

Homogeneous catalysts

A homogeneous catalyst is in the same phase (gas, liquid or solid) as the reactants. This is often a liquid, because many reactions are carried out in solution.

A good example of a reaction that involves a homogeneous catalyst is **esterification**. This has already been covered in Module 2812. The reaction is between ethanol (a liquid) and ethanoic acid (a liquid). Sulphuric acid (a liquid) is the homogeneous catalyst.

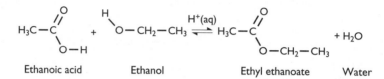

| Ethanoic acid | Ethanol | Ethyl ethanoate | Water |

The acid catalyst, $H^+(aq)$, works by providing an alternative mechanism involving an activated intermediate of lower activation energy. The $H^+(aq)$ ions from the catalyst take part in the reaction, but are released at the end of the reaction so that the concentration of the acid catalyst is the same as at the start.

A second example of a reaction involving a homogeneous catalyst is the destruction of ozone in the upper atmosphere (stratosphere). This is a gas phase reaction. The catalyst is the chlorine free radical, $Cl\bullet(g)$. Chlorine free radicals are formed when the C–Cl bonds in CFCs (see the guide to Module 2812) are subject to high-energy ultraviolet light. The complex reactions are summarised below.

$$Cl\bullet(g) + O_3(g) \longrightarrow ClO\bullet(g) + O_2(g)$$
$$ClO\bullet(g) + O_3(g) \longrightarrow Cl\bullet(g) + 2O_2(g)$$

The net reaction for this process is shown below.

$$2O_3(g) \xrightarrow[\text{as catalyst}]{Cl\bullet(g)} 3O_2(g)$$

Heterogeneous catalysts

Heterogeneous catalysts are in a different phase from the reactants. They also lower activation energy, but their mode of action is different from that of homogeneous catalysts.

The most common type of heterogeneous catalysis involves reactions of gases in the presence of a solid catalyst. The catalyst works by adsorbing the gases onto its solid surface. This adsorption results in a weakening of the bonds within the reactant molecules, which lowers the activation energy. Bonds are broken, new bonds are formed and the product molecules are desorbed from the solid surface of the catalyst.

Transition metals are frequently used as heterogeneous catalysts. Iron is used as the catalyst in the Haber process for the production of ammonia (see page 35). The iron is usually either finely divided (and therefore has a large surface area) or porous iron, containing a small amount of metal oxide promoters.

$$N_2(g) + 3H_2(g) \xrightarrow[\text{as catalyst}]{\text{Fe(s)}} 2NH_3(g)$$

Catalysts are of great economic and industrial importance and are used in a wide variety of manufacturing processes. They increase the rate of reaction and often lead to lower production costs. They can be recovered at the end of the process. Catalysts are used in a diverse range of reactions such as:

- production of ammonia, NH_3, in the Haber process. Fe is used as a catalyst.
- processing of petroleum into more efficient fuels by cracking, isomerisation and reforming. The catalysts used are often zeolites, which are compounds of sodium aluminium silicates.
- production of margarine from the hydrogenation of polyunsaturated compounds derived from natural oils. The catalysts used are transition metals, such as nickel.

Catalytic converters

The internal combustion engine discharges many pollutants into the atmosphere. Car engines may discharge unreacted hydrocarbons into the atmosphere. Some of these, for example benzene, are toxic and carcinogenic. Carbon monoxide is also formed by the incomplete combustion of fuel.

$$C_8H_{18} + 8\tfrac{1}{2}O_2 \longrightarrow 8CO + 9H_2O$$

The internal combustion engine often reaches temperatures of around 1000°C. This high temperature provides sufficient energy for nitrogen and oxygen (both present in the air) to react, forming oxides of nitrogen.

$$N_2 + O_2 \longrightarrow 2NO$$
$$2NO + O_2 \longrightarrow 2NO_2$$

Carbon monoxide, nitrogen monoxide, nitrogen dioxide and unburnt hydrocarbons can lead to the formation of photochemical smog. Under certain conditions, such as bright sunlight and still air, this can lead to the production of low-level ozone. High-level ozone, in the upper atmosphere, is beneficial, but low-level ozone traps pollutant gases.

However, the development of the **catalytic converter** has contributed significantly to the improvement in air quality. Catalytic converters are fitted to modern cars and reduce the emission of unburnt hydrocarbons, carbon monoxide and oxides of nitrogen, as shown below.

Removal of unburnt hydrocarbons:

$$C_8H_{18}(g) + 12\tfrac{1}{2}O_2(g) \longrightarrow 8CO_2(g) + 9H_2O(g)$$

Removal of carbon monoxide:

$$2NO(g) + 2CO(g) \longrightarrow N_2(g) + 2CO_2(g)$$

Removal of oxides of nitrogen:

$$2NO_2(g) + 4CO(g) \longrightarrow N_2(g) + 4CO_2(g)$$

The reactions are in the gas phase. The catalytic converter is a fine aluminium mesh coated with a thin, solid film of an alloy of platinum, rhodium and palladium. Catalytic converters only function efficiently at high temperatures, so they are not very effective on short journeys.

Chemical equilibrium

Reversible reactions

There are many everyday examples of reversible reactions or processes, the best known being the changes between the physical states of H_2O. If the temperature of water falls below $0\,°C$, the water freezes and ice forms. When the temperature rises above $0\,°C$, the ice melts and water forms again. This process can be represented as:

$$H_2O(s) \rightleftharpoons H_2O(l)$$

The $\rightleftharpoons$ sign indicates that the reaction is reversible. Reversible reactions are quite common. Another example is esterification.

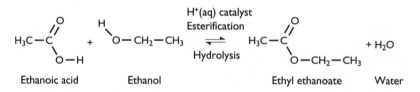

Ethanoic acid   Ethanol   Ethyl ethanoate   Water

In the presence of an acid catalyst, ethanoic acid reacts with ethanol to produce the ester ethyl ethanoate and water. Ethyl ethanoate is hydrolysed by water, in the presence of an acid catalyst, to produce ethanoic acid and ethanol.

Dynamic equilibrium

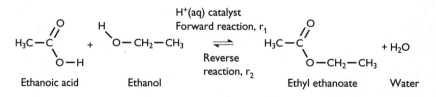

Ethanoic acid   Ethanol   Ethyl ethanoate   Water

In the reversible reaction shown above, the reaction from left to right is called the forward reaction; the reaction from right to left is the reverse reaction.

If ethanoic acid and ethanol are refluxed in the presence of an acid catalyst, the forward reaction is initially fast, because the concentration of both reagents is high. However, as they react, the concentration of each decreases, lowering the rate of the forward reaction.

The reverse reaction is initially very slow because the amount of ethyl ethanoate and water present is very small. However, as time progresses, the concentration of ethyl ethanoate and water gradually increases, as does the rate of the reverse reaction.

In summary, the forward reaction starts off fast but slows down, while the reverse reaction starts slowly and speeds up. It follows that a point will be reached when the rate of the forward reaction exactly equals the rate of the reverse reaction. When this happens, the system is in **dynamic equilibrium**.

- **Equilibrium** has been reached because the amount of each chemical in the system remains constant.
- The equilibrium is **dynamic** because the reagents and the products are constantly interchanging. A dynamic equilibrium can only be reached if the system is closed.

A good visual representation of a dynamic equilibrium is a 'mexican wave', often seen at football matches. The wave clearly moves around the stadium (**dynamic**), but as one person stands up, another sits down (**equilibrium**). The number of people standing and the number of people sitting is constant, but the individuals standing are constantly changing.

A dynamic equilibrium is reached when the rate of the forward reaction equals the rate of the reverse reaction, the concentration of the reagents and products remaining constant while the reagent and product molecules constantly interchange. This is a useful definition to learn for examinations.

Le Chatelier's principle

The French chemist Henri Le Chatelier studied many dynamic equilibria and suggested a general, qualitative rule that can be used to predict the movement of the position of the equilibrium. Le Chatelier's principle states that if a closed system under equilibrium is subject to a change, the system will move to *minimise* the effect of the change.

The factors that can be readily changed are concentration, temperature and pressure.
- If we increase the concentration, the system will move to decrease the concentration.
- If we increase the temperature, the system will move to decrease the temperature.
- If we decrease the pressure, the system will move to increase the pressure.

In many ways, Le Chatelier's principle seems to describe the behaviour of my children. Whatever I say, they will do the opposite!

The effect of changing concentration on the equilibrium position

The equilibrium formed between the chromate ion, CrO_4^{2-}, and the dichromate ion, $Cr_2O_7^{2-}$, is useful because each ion is coloured and so it is possible to observe the movement of the position of the equilibrium.

$$2H^+ + 2CrO_4^{2-} \rightleftharpoons Cr_2O_7^{2-} + H_2O$$
$$\text{yellow} \qquad \text{orange}$$

Adding acid to the chromate/dichromate mixture increases the concentration of hydrogen ions. The system now moves to minimise the effect, i.e. it tries to decrease the concentration of H^+. This is achieved by the additional H^+ ions reacting with some of the CrO_4^{2-} ions to form the products, $Cr_2O_7^{2-}$ and H_2O.

Adding an acid to the system above causes the yellow solution to turn orange, i.e. the system moves from left to right.

Another example is the large-scale manufacture of ammonia by the Haber process.

$$N_2(g) + 3H_2(g) \rightleftharpoons 2NH_3(g)$$

The boiling points of the gases are shown in the table.

Gas	Boiling point
Nitrogen	77 K (−196 °C)
Hydrogen	20 K (−253 °C)
Ammonia	240 K (−33 °C)

If the equilibrium mixture is cooled to about −40 °C, the ammonia gas liquefies. This means that ammonia gas is lost from the equilibrium mixture — its concentration decreases. The system moves to minimise the effect of this loss, i.e. the reagents react to produce more NH_3 gas to replace that liquefied out of the system.

The effect of changing pressure on the equilibrium position

Changing pressure has virtually no effect on the reactions of solids or liquids. It only affects gaseous reactions.

The pressure of a gas mixture depends on the number of molecules in the mixture. The greater the number of gas molecules in the equilibrium mixture, the greater is the pressure in the equilibrium mixture. If the pressure is increased, a system at equilibrium alters to decrease the pressure by reducing the number of gas molecules in the system.

If the pressure is increased in a system such as $2SO_2(g) + O_2(g) \rightleftharpoons 2SO_3(g)$, the position of the equilibrium moves to the *right*, so that the number of molecules is reduced. This has the effect of reducing the pressure.

If the pressure is increased in a system such as $N_2O_4(g) \rightleftharpoons 2NO_2(g)$, the position of the equilibrium moves to the *left*, so that the number of molecules is reduced. This has the effect of reducing the pressure.

If the pressure is increased in a system such as $2HI(g) \rightleftharpoons H_2(g) + I_2(g)$, the position of the equilibrium does *not move*, because there is the same number of molecules on each side of the equilibrium. A change in the equilibrium position has no effect on the pressure.

The effect of changing temperature on the equilibrium position

Temperature not only influences the rate of the reaction; it also plays an important role in determining the equilibrium position. The effect of temperature can only be predicted if the ΔH value of the reaction is known.

Consider the reaction:

$$2A(g) + B(g) \rightleftharpoons C(g) + D(g) \qquad \Delta H = -100\,kJ\,mol^{-1}$$

It follows that:

- the forward reaction, $2A(g) + B(g) \longrightarrow C(g) + D(g)$, $\Delta H = -100\,kJ\,mol^{-1}$, is exothermic
- the reverse reaction, $C(g) + D(g) \longrightarrow 2A(g) + B(g)$, $\Delta H = +100\,kJ\,mol^{-1}$, is endothermic

According to Le Chatelier's principle, if we increase the temperature for the reaction mixture, the system will try to decrease the temperature. The equilibrium mixture can achieve this by favouring the reverse reaction, which is endothermic. An endothermic reaction takes in energy from the surroundings and so reduces the temperature. Effectively, it tries to minimise the external increase in temperature. The equilibrium position, therefore, moves in the endothermic direction, in this case to the left.

Decomposition of hydrogen iodide is an **endothermic** reaction.

$$2HI(g) \rightleftharpoons H_2(g) + I_2(g)$$

Therefore:

- if temperature is increased, the equilibrium moves to the right
- if temperature is decreased, the equilibrium moves to the left

Oxidation of sulphur dioxide is an **exothermic** reaction.

$$SO_2(g) + O_2(g) \rightleftharpoons 2SO_3(g)$$

Therefore:

- if temperature is increased, the equilibrium moves to the left
- if temperature is decreased, the equilibrium moves to the right

The effect of using a catalyst on the equilibrium position

A catalyst is a substance that speeds up a reaction by lowering the activation energy, without itself being changed. A catalyst does *not* alter the amount of product produced.

In a system at equilibrium, a catalyst speeds up the forward and the reverse reaction equally and therefore has *no effect* on the equilibrium position. However, catalysts play an important part in reversible reactions, because they reduce the time taken to reach equilibrium.

In summary, the presence of a catalyst results in the same amount of product being produced more quickly.

The Haber process

Large quantities of nitrogen compounds, particularly fertilisers, are needed by society. Atmospheric nitrogen is in plentiful supply, but cannot be used directly and must be converted (fixed) into useful compounds. The Haber process 'fixes' atmospheric nitrogen, converting it into ammonia.

$$N_2(g) + 3H_2(g) \rightleftharpoons 2NH_3(g)$$
$$\Delta H = -93\,kJ\,mol^{-1}$$

Le Chatelier's principle enables us to predict the optimum conditions for this industrial process.

ΔH is $-93\,kJ\,mol^{-1}$, so the forward reaction is exothermic.

Therefore:
- if temperature is increased, the equilibrium moves to the left
- if temperature is decreased, the equilibrium moves to the right

Therefore, the optimum temperature for maximum yield of ammonia is a low temperature.

If the pressure is increased on a system such as $N_2(g) + 3H_2(g) \rightleftharpoons 2NH_3(g)$, the position of the equilibrium moves to the *right*, so that the number of molecules is reduced. This has the effect of reducing the pressure. Therefore, the optimum pressure for maximum yield of ammonia is a high pressure.

The table below illustrates the effect of changing temperature and pressure on the percentage yield of ammonia.

Temperature	Pressure			
	25 atm	50 atm	100 atm	200 atm
373 K	92	94	96	98
573 K	28	40	53	67
773 K	3	6	11	18
973 K	1	2	4	9

Low temperature (373 K = 100 °C) gives the highest percentage yield. However, at low temperature, the rate of reaction is slow and a compromise has to be reached between yield and rate of reaction.

High pressure (200 atm) gives the highest percentage yield. High pressure also increases the rate of reaction. However, at high pressure, the operating costs increase and a compromise has to be reached between yield/rate and costs.

The manufacture of ammonia in a modern plant is highly efficient. The operating conditions are:
- a temperature of around 700 K (427 °C)
- a pressure of around 100 atm

The temperature and pressure used industrially are compromise conditions. The rate of reaction is increased by using a finely divided or porous iron catalyst, which incorporates metal oxide promoters.

Ammonia is of great industrial importance and is used to manufacture:
- fertilisers, such as ammonium sulphate, $(NH_4)_2SO_4$
- polyamides, such as nylon, $-[(CH_2)_6NHCO(CH_2)_6CONH]_n-$
- explosives, such as 2,4,6-trinitromethylbenzene, $(NO_2)_3C_6H_2(CH_3)$, which is better known as TNT
- pharmaceuticals, such as paracetamol, and artificial sweeteners, such as aspartame

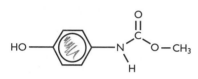

Paracetamol

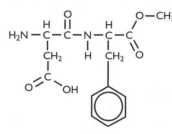

Aspartame

✗ Acid–base equilibria: strong and weak acids

An acid is defined as a species that can donate a proton. Examples include:
- hydrochloric acid (HCl)
- sulphuric acid (H_2SO_4)
- ethanoic acid (CH_3COOH)

A base is defined as a species that can accept a proton. Examples include:
- sodium hydroxide (NaOH)
- potassium hydroxide (KOH)
- ammonia (NH_3)

Strong acids are acids that dissociate completely into their ions, while weak acids only dissociate partially into their ions. The difference in the degree of dissociation can be shown by the type of arrow used to represent strong or weak acids in equations.

$\longrightarrow$ indicates complete dissociation, and is used with a strong acid like HCl:
$$HCl(aq) \longrightarrow H^+(aq) + Cl^-(aq)$$

$\rightleftharpoons$ indicates partial dissociation, and is used with a weak acid like CH_3COOH:
$$CH_2COOH(aq) \rightleftharpoons CH_3COO^-(aq) + H^+(aq)$$

Reactions of acids

Both strong and weak acids react with some metals, carbonates, bases or alkalis to form **salts**, as shown in the following table.

Reaction	Balanced equation	Ionic equation
Acid and metal	$2HCl(aq) + Zn(s)$ $\longrightarrow ZnCl_2(aq) + H_2(g)$	$2H^+(aq) + Zn(s)$ $\longrightarrow Zn^{2+}(aq) + H_2(g)$
Acid and carbonate	$2HCl(aq) + Na_2CO_3(aq)$ $\longrightarrow 2NaCl(aq) + H_2O(l) + CO_2(g)$	$2H^+(aq) + CO_3^{2-}(aq)$ $\longrightarrow H_2O(l) + CO_2(g)$
Acid and base	$2HCl(aq) + MgO(s)$ $\longrightarrow MgCl_2(aq) + H_2O(l)$	$2H^+(aq) + MgO(s)$ $\longrightarrow Mg^{2+}(aq) + H_2O(l)$
Acid and alkali	$HCl(aq) + NaOH(aq)$ $\longrightarrow NaCl(aq) + H_2O(l)$	$H^+(aq) + OH^-(aq)$ $\longrightarrow H_2O(l)$

Ammonia is an important base. The salt, ammonium sulphate, is formed by the reaction of ammonia with sulphuric acid. Ammonium sulphate is used in fertilisers.

- Balanced equation:

$$2NH_3(aq) + H_2SO_4(aq) \longrightarrow (NH_4)_2SO_4(aq)$$

- Ionic equation:

$$NH_3(aq) + H^+(aq) \longrightarrow NH_4^+(aq)$$

Practical assessment

As outlined in the Introduction section of this guide, Module 2813 contains a practical element as well as Component 01: How Far, How Fast? Candidates follow either Component 02 (practical assessment carried out in your own centre and marked by your teachers) or Component 03 (practical examination set by the examination board and marked by external examiners).

Component 02: coursework experimental skills

Skills P (planning) and A (analysing evidence and drawing conclusions) are marked out of 8 and Skills I (implementing) and E (evaluating evidence and procedures) are marked out of 7. Centres are required to award marks for each of Skills P, I, A and E. Hence the maximum mark available is 30. When a skill has been assessed on more than one occasion, at AS or A2, the best mark for that skill is submitted. The marks are then doubled, so that the final marks submitted are out of 60.

The OCR examination board suggests a range of experiments that schools and colleges can use and supplies details of how teachers should mark the assessments. The experiments suggested by OCR are shown in the table below.

Experiment	Skill P	Skill I	Skill A	Skill E
Which equation is correct?	✓			
To determine the concentration of a limewater solution	✓		✓	
Determination of the relative atomic mass of lithium		✓	✓	✓
Hydrolysis of halogenoalkanes	✓			
To determine the enthalpy change of a reaction			✓	✓
The oxidation of ethanol		✓		

Your teacher may decide to use different experiments and will have to devise a mark scheme that fits the general descriptors. Copies of these general descriptors are on pages 43–46.

Skill P: planning

Candidates should identify and define the nature of a question or problem using available information and knowledge of chemistry.

- You are expected to read around the problem and to consider a range of solutions. Your plan should *not* simply be copied from a textbook.
- You may have to carry out calculations or write balanced equations when trying to explain the 'nature of the problem'.
- You must use a range of sources to help you develop your plan. These could include textbooks, CD ROMs and the internet. It is essential that you reference each of your sources so that they can be checked. If you use a textbook you should state: the title, the author, the publisher and the page numbers. If you use the internet, the website should be quoted. To reach the higher marks, you ought to quote at least three sources.

Candidates should choose effective and safe procedures, selecting appropriate apparatus and materials and deciding the measurements and observations likely to generate useful and reliable results.

Candidates should consider the environmental and safety aspects of the proposed procedures.

Your plan should include:
- a list of apparatus and a diagram (where appropriate)
- a list of reagents/chemicals and their concentrations (where appropriate)
- evidence of awareness of any necessary safety precautions, stating the source of your information — the moderators need to see that you have read the information and thought about how it applies to your plan rather than simply copied out details from *Hazcards*
- a detailed step-by-step method that could be followed by others

Skill I: implementing

Candidates should use apparatus and materials in an appropriate and safe way.

Candidates should carry out work in a methodical and organised way with due regard for safety and with appropriate consideration for the wellbeing of the environment.

- You are expected to follow instructions.
- You are expected to work safely with due regard for others in the laboratory.
- You will lose marks if you spill chemicals, break apparatus or fail to follow the instructions.

Implementing is checked by your teachers, who may have a tick list to help them check that you have performed the experiment correctly.

Candidates should make and record detailed observations in a suitable way and make measurements to an appropriate degree of precision.

- You are expected to record your results and/or observations in a suitable format. You will not be told what the format is.
- You are expected to record your results to an appropriate degree of accuracy.
- You may have to devise a suitable table of results. The table should include suitable headings and units, where appropriate.

Skill A: analysing evidence and drawing conclusions

Candidates should communicate information and ideas, including: tabulation, line graphs, histograms, continuous prose, annotated drawings and diagrams, as appropriate.

Candidates should recognise and comment on trends and patterns in data.

You are expected:
- to carry out calculations, quoting your answers to the appropriate number of significant figures
- to draw graphs
- use appropriate units
- to take measurements to an appropriate degree of accuracy
- to analyse your results and/or observations and relate them to chemical principles or trends

Candidates should draw valid conclusions by applying chemical knowledge and understanding.

You are expected:
- to use your results, observations and analysis to make appropriate deductions
- to explain the chemical logic behind your conclusions and substantiate them with relevant chemical knowledge
- to use specialists terms, where appropriate
- to use accurate spelling, punctuation and grammar

Skill E: evaluating evidence and procedures

This is the most difficult of the skills and candidates generally find it hard to reach the higher marks.

Candidates should assess the reliability and precision of experimental data and the conclusions drawn from it.

Evaluation may be along the lines of, 'I would repeat the experiment, but use a more accurate thermometer'. This sort of statement may or may not be valid and certainly needs to be justified.

- Most scientific apparatus can be read to within half a graduation. Typically, a burette can be read to ± 0.05 cm^3, whereas a measuring cylinder can only be read to ± 0.5 cm^3.
- Typically, a thermometer can be read to within 0.5 °C. If a temperature change is 1.0 °C, this introduces an error in the order of $(0.5/1.0) \times 100 = 50\%$. However, if the same thermometer was used to measure a temperature change of 50 °C, the error is $(0.5/50) \times 100 = 1\%$.
- You are expected to assess the reliability and accuracy of the data obtained in your experiment.

Candidates should evaluate the techniques used in the experimental activity, recognising their limitations.

Evaluation may be along the lines of, 'If I had more time, I would do it again and take the average'.

- It may be appropriate to repeat an experiment and average the results in a procedure such as a titration. However, if the method itself is at fault, there is little point in repeating a flawed process. All that this achieves is the average of two equally unreliable results.
- You are expected to look critically at the method and highlight any in-built errors in the process.
- You are expected to suggest modifications to eliminate or reduce these errors.

Component 03: practical examination

External assessment of experimental and investigative skills addresses the same skills as those covered by the Coursework option. The practical examination option is in two parts. Part A is a planning exercise and is used to assess Skill P. Part B is a practical exercise and is used to assess Skills I, A and E.

You are asked to carry out an experiment set in the same general context as that used for the planning exercise, but which is *not* the same task. Thus, while the research work carried out for the planning task may assist you in your interpretation of the experimental results, you will *not* be asked to carry out the investigation you have planned.

Planning exercise

The OCR examination board assesses Skill P by asking you to plan an investigation. The task is set by the board and your teachers cannot influence which area of the specification is tested.

You are given the planning task before the practical examination. The work must be handed in on or before the day of the practical examination. Your school or college has to send your plan to the examiner with the practical examination scripts.

Access to suitable library and other resources may be required. You have from 7 to 10 days to complete your plan, which should be no longer than 1000 words.

The mark scheme for this task is closely based on the coursework mark descriptors for Skill P (see page 43).

An example of the sort of task that may be set is given below.

To determine the enthalpy changes of reaction for some reactive metals, including lithium and magnesium, with dilute hydrochloric acid.

Metals react exothermically with dilute hydrochloric acid.

You may assume that only the following chemicals are available:
- aqueous hydrochloric acid (exact concentration not known, but thought to be between 2.0 and 2.5 $mol\,dm^{-3}$)
- samples of five metals of your choice (including magnesium and lithium)
- a suitable indicator

You should:
- plan how to determine accurately the exact concentration of the hydrochloric acid
- describe how to determine the enthalpy changes in $kJ\,mol^{-1}$ for the reactions of the metals with HCl
- show clearly how you would calculate each value from your results

Your plan should include:
- evidence of relevant chemical knowledge and understanding
- a list of apparatus and chemicals needed
- a detailed method which provides full instructions, including the quantities of chemicals you would use and calculations to show how you worked out these quantities
- risk assessments and safety precautions

Any quotations direct from the work of others should be acknowledged by quotation marks. Page references should be given and the sources should be included in the bibliography.

Quality of written communication is assessed in Skill P.

Practical examination

The practical examination is on a topic related to the planning exercise. The examination is used to assess Skills I, A and E.

Skill I is assessed on the way you carry out the experiment and the observations and/or measurements taken.

Skills A and E are assessed on your analysis and evaluation of the results of the experiment. You may be given other data and information to help with this.

The mark scheme for the practical examination is closely based on the coursework mark descriptors for these skills and it is marked using the same criteria as coursework.

Mark descriptors for skills P, I, A and E

Each of the skills P, I, A and E is sub-divided into two strands, strand a and strand b. Each strand is hierarchical and you cannot reach the higher levels unless you have already achieved all of the lower levels. For instance, in order to get level 7a, you must also have achieved everything described in levels 1a, 3a and 5a.

There are no descriptors for levels 2,4 or 6. However, it is still possible to be awarded 2, 4 or 6 marks. If you achieve level 5a in strand a but only get to level 3b in strand b, then you will be given 4 marks to reflect that you are somewhere between levels 3 and 5.

Skills P and A also have level 8. This is reserved for exceptional work and is awarded rarely. Your teachers will only award a level 8 if you extend your understanding well beyond what is expected at this level.

Skill P

Mark	Level	General strategy	Level	Choices within plan
0				
1	P1a	Develops a question or problem in simple terms and plans a fair test or an appropriate practical procedure Makes a prediction, where relevant	P1b	Chooses appropriate equipment
2				

Mark	Level	General strategy	Level	Choices within plan
3	P3a	Develops a question or problem using scientific knowledge and understanding Identifies the key factors to vary, control or take account of	P3b	Decides on a suitable number and range of observations and/or measurements to be made
4				
5	P5a	Uses detailed scientific knowledge and understanding Uses information from preliminary work or a secondary source to plan an appropriate strategy, taking into account the need for safe working and justifying any prediction made	P5b	Describes a strategy, including choice of equipment, which takes into account the need to produce precise and reliable evidence Produces a clear account and uses specialist vocabulary appropriately
6				
7	P7a	Retrieves and evaluates information from a variety of sources and uses it to develop a strategy which is well structured, logical and linked coherently to underlying scientific knowledge and understanding Uses spelling, punctuation and grammar accurately	P7b	Justifies the strategy developed, including the choice of equipment, in terms of the need for precision and reliability
8				

Skill I

Mark	Level	Manipulation	Level	Recording
0				
1	I1a	Demonstrates competence in simple techniques and an awareness of the need for safe working	I1b	Makes and records observations and/or measurements which are adequate for the activity
2				
3	I3a	Demonstrates competence in practised techniques Is able to manipulate materials and equipment with precision	I3b	Makes systematic and accurate observations and/or measurements which are recorded clearly and accurately

Mark	Level	Manipulation	Level	Recording
4				
5	I5a	Demonstrates competence and confidence in the use of practical techniques Adopts safe working practices throughout	I5b	Makes observations and/or measurements with precision and skill Records observations and/or measurements in an appropriate format
6				
7	I7a	Demonstrates skilful and proficient use of all techniques and equipment	I7b	Makes and records all observations and/or measurements in appropriate detail and to the degree of precision permitted by the techniques or apparatus

Skill A

Mark	Level	Processing evidence	Level	Drawing conclusions
0				
1	A1a	Carries out some simple processing of the evidence collected from experimental work	A1b	Where appropriate, identifies trends or patterns in the evidence and draws simple conclusions
2				
3	A3a	Processes and presents evidence gathered from experimental work including, where appropriate, the use of graphical and/or numerical techniques	A3b	Links conclusions drawn from processed evidence with the associated scientific knowledge and understanding
4				
5	A5a	Carries out detailed processing of evidence and analysis including, where appropriate, the use of advanced numerical techniques such as statistics, the plotting of intercepts or the calculation of gradients	A5b	Draws conclusions which are consistent with the processed evidence and links these with detailed scientific knowledge and understanding Produces a clear account, which uses specialist vocabulary appropriately
6				

Mark	Level	Processing evidence	Level	Drawing conclusions
7	A7a	Where appropriate, uses detailed scientific knowledge and understanding to make deductions from the processed evidence, with due regard to nomenclature, terminology and the use of significant figures (where relevant)	A7b	Draws conclusions which are well structured, appropriate, comprehensive and concise and which are coherently linked to underlying scientific knowledge and understanding Uses spelling, punctuation and grammar accurately
8				

Skill E

Mark	Level	Procedures	Level	Sources of error
0				
1	E1a	Makes relevant comments on the suitability of the experimental procedures	E1b	Recognises any anomalous results
2				
3	E3a	Recognises how limitations in the experimental procedures and/or strategy may result in sources of error	E3b	Comments on the accuracy of the observations and/or measurements, suggesting reasons for any anomalous results
4				
5	E5a	Indicates the significant limitations of the experimental procedures and/or strategy and suggests how they could be improved	E5b	Comments on the reliability of the evidence and evaluates the main sources of error
6				
7	E7a	Justifies proposed improvements to the experimental procedures and/or strategy in terms of increasing the reliability of the evidence and minimising significant sources of error	E7b	Assesses the significance of the uncertainties in the evidence in terms of their effect on the validity of the final conclusions drawn

Questions
&
Answers

This section contains questions similar in style to those you can expect to see in Unit Test 3. The limited number of questions means that it is impossible to cover all the topics and all the question styles, but they should give you a flavour of what to expect. The responses that are shown are real students' answers to the questions.

There are several ways of using this section. You could:
- hide the answers to each question and try the question yourself. It needn't be a memory test — use your notes to see if you can actually make all the points that you ought to make
- check your answers against the candidates' responses and make an estimate of the likely standard of your response to each question
- check your answers against the examiner's comments to see if you can appreciate where you might have lost marks
- take on the role of the examiner and mark each of the responses yourself and then check to see if you agree with the marks awarded by the examiner

The unit test lasts 45 minutes and there is a total of 45 marks. Time is very tight, so it is important that you practise answering questions under timed conditions as part of your revision.

Examiner's comments

All candidate responses are followed by examiner's comments. These are preceded by the icon *e* and indicate where credit is due. In the weaker answers, they also point out areas for improvement, specific problems and common errors such as lack of clarity, weak or non-existent development, irrelevance, misinterpretation of the question and mistaken meanings of terms.

Activation energy

The diagram below shows the energy distribution of reactant molecules at a temperature T_1.

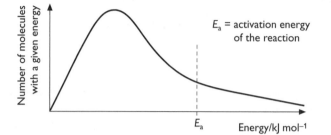

(a) Explain what is meant by the term activation energy. (2 marks)

(b) Mark on the diagram above the activation energy in the presence of a catalyst, E_c. (1 mark)

(c) Explain, in terms of the distribution curve, how a catalyst speeds up the rate of a
reaction. (2 marks)

(d) (i) Raising the temperature can also increase the rate of this reaction. Draw a
second curve to represent the energy distribution at a higher temperature.
Label your curve T_2. (2 marks)

(ii) Explain how an increase in temperature can speed up the rate of a reaction. (2 marks)

Total: 9 marks

Candidates' answers to Question 1

Candidate A

(a) The activation energy is the minimum energy needed to start a reaction.

Candidate B

(a) The energy needed for a collision to be successful.

  📝 Candidate A scores 2 marks but Candidate B only scores 1. Examination technique is
important. There are 2 marks available and the examiner is looking for two points:
minimum ✓ energy needed ✓ in a collision if particles are to react.

Candidate A

(b)

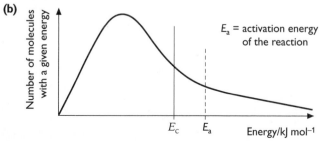

question

Candidate B

(b)

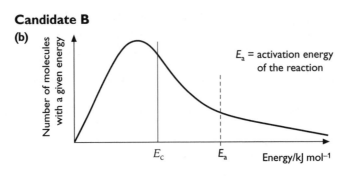

E_a = activation energy of the reaction

E_c E_a Energy/kJ mol^{-1}

Both gain the mark. The activation energy with the catalyst present must be lower than the original activation energy.

Candidate A

(c) The mode of action of any catalyst is to lower the activation energy so that more particles have enough energy to react.

Candidate B

(c) A catalyst is a substance that speeds up a reaction without itself being altered. Catalysts can be homogeneous (same phase) or heterogeneous (different phase). Catalysts can be reused.

Candidate A gains both marks but Candidate B scores nothing. Candidate B has not read the question carefully and has simply written down correct statements about catalysts, none of which is relevant to the question.

Candidate A

(d) (i)

E_a = activation energy of the reaction

T_2

E_c E_a Energy/kJ mol^{-1}

Candidate B

(d) (i)

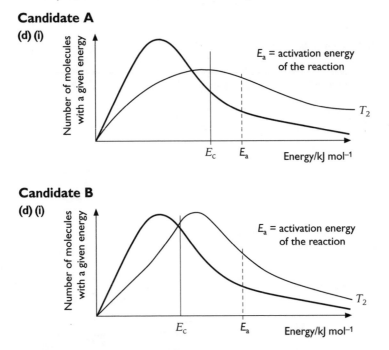

E_a = activation energy of the reaction

T_2

E_c E_a Energy/kJ mol^{-1}

e Candidate A gains both marks, but Candidate B only gains 1. For 1 mark, both candidates show that at increased temperature, the distribution moves to the right (to higher energy). However, as the distribution moves to the right, the curve also flattens out. Candidate A's sketch shows this, while Candidate B's does not.

Candidate A

(d) (ii) Increasing temperature increases energy. Therefore, more particles will have energy greater than or equal to the minimum energy required, so the reaction will speed up.

Candidate B

(d) (ii) Increasing temperature lowers the activation energy and therefore more particles exceed the activation energy.

e Candidate A gives the perfect response and gains both marks. Candidate B has misunderstood what effect increasing temperature has on the activation energy and has probably confused it with the effect of a catalyst. Unfortunately, this answer scores no marks. Catalysts lower the activation energy but changing the temperature has no effect on activation energy.

e **Candidate A scores the maximum 9 marks, but Candidate B only scores 3. Candidate B's mark is equivalent to a borderline grade E, but with a little care the score could have increased by 3 or 4 marks to a high grade C or even grade B.**

Bond enthalpy and catalysts

Bond enthalpies provide information about the energy changes that accompany a chemical reaction.

(a) What do you understand by the term bond enthalpy? (3 marks)

(b) (i) Write an equation, including state symbols, to represent the bond enthalpy in hydrogen chloride. (2 marks)

(ii) Write an equation to represent the bond enthalpy in methane. (3 marks)

The table below shows some average bond enthalpies.

Bond	Average bond enthalpy/kJ mol^{-1}
C–C	350
C=C	610
H–H	436
C–H	410

(c) (i) Use the information in the table to calculate the enthalpy change for the hydrogenation of ethene.

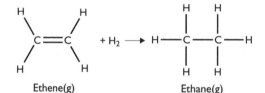

Ethene(g) Ethane(g)

(3 marks)

(ii) The enthalpy change of this reaction is found by experiment to be −136 kJ mol^{-1}. Explain why this value is different from that determined above. (2 marks)

(d) (i) In the above reaction, nickel is used as a catalyst. Define a catalyst. (2 marks)

(ii) State whether nickel is a homogeneous or a heterogeneous catalyst in this reaction. (1 mark)

(iii) Explain the mode of action of nickel in this reaction. (3 marks)

Total: 19 marks

■ ■ ■

Candidates' answers to Question 2

Candidate A

(a) It is the enthalpy change when 1 mole of covalent bonds is broken in the gaseous state.

Candidate B

(a) The energy needed to break 1 mole of a bond in the gas state.

📝 The 3 marks are allocated for the idea that bond enthalpy involves breaking ✓ bonds and that the quantity of bond broken is 1 mole ✓ in the gaseous state ✓. Both candidates score all 3 marks.

Candidate A

(b) (i) $HCl(g) \longrightarrow H(g) + Cl(g)$

Candidate B

(b) (i) $HCl \longrightarrow H + Cl$

📝 Candidate A scores both marks. Candidate B omits the state symbols and therefore loses 1 mark.

Candidate A

(b) (ii) $CH_4(g) \longrightarrow CH_3(g) + H(g)$

Candidate B

(b) (ii) $CH_4(g) \longrightarrow C(g) + 4H(g)$

📝 Neither candidate scores all 3 marks. Part (b) (i) merited 2 marks — 1 for the equation and 1 for the state symbols. This question does not ask for state symbols and, therefore, the answer must involve considerably more than is presented here. Candidate A has used the definition of bond enthalpy literally and has 'broken 1 bond in the gaseous state' but because methane has four C–H bonds, the bond enthalpy is the average of all four bond enthalpies. Candidate A is awarded 1 mark. Candidate B has shown the enthalpy change for breaking four C–H bonds and not 1 and is also awarded 1 mark. The equation the examiners were looking for is:

$$\tfrac{1}{4}(CH(g) \longrightarrow C(g) + 4H(g))$$

which clearly indicates that the bond enthalpy in methane is the average bond enthalpy taken when all 4 C–H bonds are broken. This is shown below.

$$CH_4(g) \longrightarrow CH_3(g) + H(g) \qquad \Delta H = +425 \text{ kJ mol}^{-1}$$
$$CH_3(g) \longrightarrow CH_2(g) + H(g) \qquad \Delta H = +470 \text{ kJ mol}^{-1}$$
$$CH_2(g) \longrightarrow CH(g) + H(g) \qquad \Delta H = +416 \text{ kJ mol}^{-1}$$
$$CH(g) \longrightarrow C(g) + H(g) \qquad \Delta H = +335 \text{ kJ mol}^{-1}$$

The total enthalpy change is $(+425 + 470 + 416 + 335) = +1646 \text{ kJ mol}^{-1}$, which is the enthalpy change when four C–H bonds are broken in methane. Therefore, the enthalpy change when one C–H bond is broken is $+1646/4 = +411.5 \text{ kJ mol}^{-1}$. Clearly, candidates are *not* expected to quote numerical values but they are expected to realise that the bond enthalpy quoted is the average value.

Candidate A

(c) (i) Bonds broken: $(610 + 1640 + 436) = +2686$
Bonds formed: $(-350 - 2460) = -2810$
Enthalpy change $= -124 \text{ kJ mol}^{-1}$

Candidate B

(c) (i) Bonds broken: $C=C = +610$
Bonds formed: $2 \times C–H = -820$; $1 \times C–C = -350$
Enthalpy change $= -560 \text{ kJ mol}^{-1}$

There are two ways of carrying out this calculation. Candidate A has opted for the safest way and calculated the enthalpy change for breaking every bond in the reactants and then for forming every bond in the product. A sensible way to set this out is to list every bond:

Bonds broken: $1 \times$ C=C $= + 610$; $4 \times$ C–H $= + 1640$; $1 \times$ H–H $= +436$

Bonds formed: $1 \times$ C–C $= -350$; $6 \times$ C–H $= -2460$

Enthalpy change $= -124$ kJ mol^{-1}

Candidate B has looked at the overall change and attempted to identify the net change in bonds broken and formed. He/she has correctly worked out that if four C–H bonds are broken and six C–H bonds are formed, the net change is the formation of two C–H bonds. However, Candidate B has forgotten that H_2 contains an H–H bond, which also has to be broken. Candidate A gains all 3 marks and Candidate B gains 2, even though the answer is incorrect. The answer has been marked 'consequentially'; as there is only one error in the calculation, Candidate B loses only 1 mark.

Candidate A

(c) (ii) The bond energies used in the calculation are average values for the bonds.

Candidate B

(c) (ii) Experiments are not very accurate and heat will be lost.

 Candidate A gains 1 mark. The second mark is for an explanation that the C–H bond in ethene is not the same as the C–H bond in ethane because they are in different environments. Candidate B has made assumptions about the accuracy of the experiment that are not justified, and scores no marks.

Candidate A

(d) (i) A catalyst speeds up a reaction without being used up.

Candidate B

(d) (i) A catalyst speeds up a reaction by lowering the activation energy.

 Both candidates score 2 marks.

Candidate A

(d) (ii) Heterogeneous

Candidate B

(d) (ii) Heterogeneous

 Both candidates are correct, for 1 mark.

Candidate A

(d) (iii) The ethene and hydrogen gases are absorbed by the nickel, the reaction takes place and the ethane is desorbed.

Candidate B

(d) (iii) The reactants bind to the surface of the nickel (adsorb) and the bonds are weakened. The reaction takes place and the product leaves the surface of the nickel (desorbs).

🖉 The marking points are: adsorbs to nickel surface ✓; weakens bonds or lowers activation energy ✓; desorbs from nickel surface ✓. Candidate A only gains 1 mark. Using the word 'absorbed' means the first marking point is lost and no reference is made as to how the bonds are weakened. Candidate B scores all 3 marks.

🖉 **These are both good answers, with Candidate A scoring 15 and Candidate B gaining 13 out of 19 marks. Both are on the B/C borderline, but with a little extra care each candidate could have picked up an extra 2 or 3 marks, pushing them up to grade A standard.**

Enthalpy of combustion and catalysis

Octane, C_8H_{18}, is one of the hydrocarbons present in petrol.

(a) Define the term *standard enthalpy change of combustion*. (3 marks)

(b) Use the data below to calculate the standard enthalpy change of combustion of octane.

Compound	$\Delta H / kJ\,mol^{-1}$
$C_8H_{18}(l)$	−250.0
$CO_2(g)$	−393.5
$H_2O(l)$	−285.9

$$C_8H_{18}(l) + 12\tfrac{1}{2}O_2(g) \longrightarrow 8CO_2(g) + 9H_2O(l)$$ (3 marks)

(c) Combustion in a car engine also produces polluting gases, mainly carbon monoxide, unburnt hydrocarbons and oxides of nitrogen such as nitrogen monoxide, **NO**. Explain, with the aid of equations, how **CO** and **NO** are produced in a car engine. (2 marks)

(d) (i) The catalytic converter removes much of these potential pollutants by a series of reactions. Write an equation showing the removal of **CO** and **NO** gases. (1 mark)

(ii) The removal of **CO** and **NO** gases involves a redox reaction. Use your answer to (d)(i) to identify the element being reduced and state the change in its oxidation number. (2 marks)

Total: 11 marks

■ ■ ■

Candidates' answers to Question 3

Candidate A

(a) It is the enthalpy change when 1 mole of a substance is burnt completely, in an excess of oxygen, under standard conditions of 298 K and 1 atmosphere.

Candidate B

(a) It is the enthalpy change when 1 mole of a substance is burnt in oxygen, under standard conditions.

✐ Candidate A scores all 3 marks. The marking points are: 1 mole ✓; burnt in an excess of oxygen ✓; standard conditions are 298 K/25 °C and 100 kPa/1 atm ✓. Candidate B only gets 1 mark. This is probably down to carelessness and poor examination technique rather than a lack of knowledge.

Candidate A

(b)

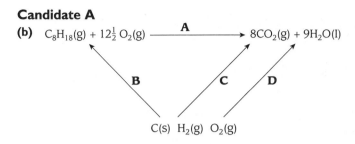

$A = C + D - B = -5471.1\,kJ\,mol^{-1}$

Candidate B

(b)

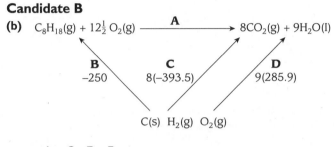

$A = C + D - B$

$= (-3148) + (2573.1) - (-250)$

$= -3148 + 2573.1 + 250$

$= -324.9\,kJ\,mol^{-1}$

e Candidate B shows good examination technique by showing all the working. Unfortunately, he/she has made a careless slip by forgetting to put the minus sign in front of 285.9 for the formation of water. The examiner can clearly see this error and is able to follow it through. Therefore, Candidate B gains 2 of the 3 marks. Candidate A gains all 3 marks. However, if the numerical value had been incorrect Candidate A would only have scored 1 mark, or possibly no marks at all. It is always better to show all of your working in any calculation.

Candidate A

(c) $C_8H_{18}(l) + 8\frac{1}{2}O_2(g) \longrightarrow 8CO(g) + 9H_2O(l)$
$N_2(g) + O_2(g) \longrightarrow 2NO(g)$

Candidate B

(c) $C_8H_{18} + 9\frac{1}{2}O_2 + N_2 \longrightarrow 8CO + 9H_2O + 2NO$

e Both candidates score 2 marks. Candidate B's response is a little unusual, but nevertheless correct.

Candidate A

(d) (i) $2NO(g) + 2CO(g) \longrightarrow N_2(g) + 2CO_2(g)$

Candidate B

(d) (i) $2NO + 2CO \longrightarrow N_2 + 2CO_2$

@ Both candidates gain the mark. Marks for state symbols are only awarded or deducted if they are asked for in the question.

Candidate A

(d) (ii) Nitrogen has been reduced because its oxidation state has changed from +2 to zero.

Candidate B

(d) (ii) $\overset{+2\,-2}{2NO} + \overset{+2\,-2}{2CO} \longrightarrow \overset{0}{N_2} + \overset{+4\,-2}{2CO_2}$

Therefore, N has been reduced.

@ Both candidates score 2 marks. Candidate A has not shown any working and, had the answer been wrong, would have lost both marks. Candidate B demonstrates better examination technique by writing the oxidation numbers along the top of the equation, so that the examiner can follow the working.

@ **Candidate A gains full marks, but has lived dangerously by not showing any working. This is essential in any calculation. If candidates show their working and make a mistake, this can be identified by the examiner and credit (marks) can be given for the method. However, if no working is shown, the only alternative is for the examiner to award full marks if the answer is correct, or to award no marks if the answer is incorrect. Candidate B shows better examination technique, but then manages to lose marks through carelessness.**

Equilibria, acids and bases

Sulphuric acid, H_2SO_4, is made industrially by the contact process, which is an example of a dynamic equilibrium.

$$2SO_2(g) + O_2(g) \rightleftharpoons 2SO_3(g) \quad \Delta H = -98\,kJ\,mol^{-1}$$

(a) State *two* features of a reaction with a *dynamic equilibrium*. (2 marks)

(b) State and explain what happens to the equilibrium position of this reaction as:

   (i)   the temperature is raised (2 marks)

   (ii) the pressure is increased (2 marks)

   (iii) Suggest the optimum conditions for the contact process. (2 marks)

(c) (i)   The conditions used for the contact process are a temperature between 450 °C and 600 °C and a pressure of about 10 atmospheres. Explain why the optimum conditions are not used. (3 marks)

   (ii) Vanadium(V) oxide is used as a catalyst. What effect does this have on the conversion of $SO_2(g)$ into $SO_3(g)$? (2 marks)

   (iii) At least three catalyst chambers are used to ensure maximum conversion of $SO_2(g)$. The conversion yield can exceed 98%. State two advantages of this high conversion rate. (2 marks)

(d) Much of the sulphuric acid produced is reacted with ammonia to make fertilisers such as ammonium sulphate, $(NH_4)_2SO_4$, in an acid–base reaction.

   (i)   Ammonia is a base. Explain what is meant by this term. (1 mark)

   (ii) Construct an equation for the acid–base reaction of ammonia with sulphuric acid. (1 mark)

   (iii) Farmers use ammonium sulphate for its nitrogen content. Calculate the percentage of nitrogen in $(NH_4)_2SO_4$. Quote your answer to three significant figures. (A_r: H, 1.0; N, 14.0; O, 16.0) (3 marks)

Total: 20 marks

■ ■ ■

Candidates' answers to Question 1

Candidate A

(a) The rate of the forward and reverse reactions is the same, so the amount of each chemical remains the same.

Candidate B

(a) The amount of each chemical in the system remains constant. The reagents react at the same rate as the products.

🖉 Both candidates gain 2 marks.

Candidate A

(b) (i) The equilibrium position moves to the left because the forward reaction is exothermic.

Candidate B

(b) (i) The reaction is much faster as more particles now exceed the activation energy.

e Candidate A scores both marks. Unfortunately, Candidate B has either misread or misunderstood the question and has explained the effect of increasing temperature on reaction rate. The explanation is correct, but scores no marks because it does not answer the question that was set. This is a common error.

Candidate A

(b) (ii) The equilibrium moves to the right because there are fewer molecules of gas on the right-hand side.

Candidate B

(b) (ii) Increasing pressure effectively increases the concentration and therefore the reaction will go faster.

e Candidate A gains both marks. Candidate B has again misread the question and made the same mistake as in (b) (i), costing another 2 marks.

Candidate A

(b) (iii) Low temperature and high pressure

Candidate B

(b) (iii) Low temperature and high pressure

e Both candidates score 2 marks.

Candidate A

(c) (i) At low temperature, the conversion is high but the rate of reaction is too slow. High pressure is too expensive.

Candidate B

(c) (i) Temperature — a compromise is reached between rate and conversion. At low temperature, the rate is too slow.
Pressure — a compromise is reached between cost and conversion.
Catalyst — a catalyst is used to speed up the rate of conversion so that it is cost-effective to work at low pressure.

e Candidate B gives the perfect answer and scores 3 marks. Candidate A gains 2 marks. The explanation of temperature is fine, but the explanation regarding pressure is barely adequate. The key to the answer is the *compromise* between rate and percentage of SO_3, cost and percentage of SO_3 together with the use of a catalyst.

Candidate A

(c) (ii) The catalyst speeds up the reaction, but does not change the equilibrium position.

Candidate B

(c) (ii) We get the same amount of SO_3 but we get it quicker.

e Both candidates score 2 marks.

Candidate A

(c) (iii) It is more cost-effective and reduces the amount of SO_2 pollution.

Candidate B

(c) (iii) It is more profitable and makes more money.

e Candidate A gives a very good answer and gains both marks. Candidate B says the same thing twice and so only scores 1 mark.

Candidate A

(d) (i) It can accept a proton.

Candidate B

(d) (i) H^+ acceptor

e Both candidates gain the mark.

Candidate A

(d) (ii) $2NH_3 + H_2SO_4 \longrightarrow (NH_4)_2SO_4$

Candidate B

(d) (ii) $2NH_3 + H_2SO_4 \longrightarrow (NH_4)_2SO_4$

e Correct, for 1 mark.

Candidate A

(d) (iii) $(NH_4)_2SO_4 = 14 + 14 + 8 + 32 + 64 = 132$
  % N = $(28/132) \times 100 = 21.212121$

Candidate B

(d) (iii) 22.1%

e Candidate A has displayed good examination technique — showing all the working — but has failed to quote the answer to three significant figures, and therefore loses 1 mark. Candidate B gets no marks and again shows poor examination technique. The correct answer is 21.2%. It is likely that Candidate B has incorrectly copied the answer from the calculator, but the examiner cannot assume this and, therefore, has no choice but to award no marks. If Candidate B had shown the working, it would have been possible to give 2 out of the 3 marks, even with the incorrect answer.

e **Candidate A scores 18 out of 20 marks. It is worth remembering that approximately 80% of the available marks equates to a grade A, 70% to a B, 60% to a C and so on. Candidate B scores 12 marks in this question, which is approximately a grade C answer. However, if 4 marks had not been lost carelessly in parts (b) (i) and (ii), it would have been a grade A answer. Every mark is important and it is essential to read the question carefully. In the final section, (d)(iii), Candidate B could have picked up another 2 marks. The poor examination technique in parts (b) and (d) resulted in Candidate B scoring 12 marks in total, but it could have been 19 out of 20.**

Energetics and equilibria in industrial processes

Annually, millions of tonnes of ammonia are manufactured from nitrogen and hydrogen, using the Haber process. There is a plentiful supply of nitrogen, which is obtained from the air, while the hydrogen is produced by a series of reactions between methane and steam:

$CH_4(g) + H_2O(g) \rightleftharpoons 3H_2(g) + CO(g)$ using nickel oxide as a catalyst at 800°C

$CO(g) + H_2O(g) \rightleftharpoons H_2(g) + CO_2(g)$ using iron(III) oxide as a catalyst at 400°C

The hydrogen then reacts with the nitrogen:

$N_2(g) + 3H_2(g) \rightleftharpoons 2NH_3(g)$

The activation energy for the forward reaction is +68 kJ mol⁻¹.

The activation energy for the reverse reaction is +160 kJ mol⁻¹.

(a) (i) Use this information to sketch the energy profile diagram. Label clearly the activation energy for the forward reaction, E_f, and the activation energy for the reverse reaction, E_r. (3 marks)

(ii) Explain what is meant by *activation energy*. (2 marks)

(iii) Calculate the enthalpy change for the forward reaction. (2 marks)

Ammonia is of great industrial importance. 80% of all the ammonia produced is converted into fertiliser. However, a substantial amount, approximately 5%, is oxidised into nitric acid using the Ostwald process. This involves three stages, shown in the table below.

Stage	Equation	Enthalpy change
Stage 1	$4NH_3(g) + 5O_2(g) \rightleftharpoons 4NO(g) + 6H_2O(g)$	$\Delta H = -950\,kJ\,mol^{-1}$
Stage 2	$2NO(g) + O_2(g) \rightleftharpoons 2NO_2(g)$	$\Delta H = -114\,kJ\,mol^{-1}$
Stage 3	$3NO_2(g) + H_2O(g) \rightleftharpoons 2HNO_3(g) + NO(g)$	$\Delta H = -117\,kJ\,mol^{-1}$

(b) (i) With reference to the oxidation number of nitrogen in NH_3 (stage 1) and HNO_3 (stage 3), show clearly that this is an oxidation process. (3 marks)

(ii) State Le Chatelier's principle. (2 marks)

(iii) In stage 1, use Le Chatelier's principle to predict and explain the temperature and pressure that would give maximum yield. (4 marks)

(iv) Suggest what happens to the NO produced in stage 3. (1 mark)

(c) The nitric acid produced in stage 3 is a strong acid. Explain, with the aid of an equation, what is meant by the term *strong acid*. (2 marks)

(d) Write a balanced equation, including state symbols, for the reaction between nitric acid and calcium carbonate. Describe what you would see in this reaction. (4 marks)

Total: 23 marks

Candidates' answers to Question 5

Candidate A

(a) (i)

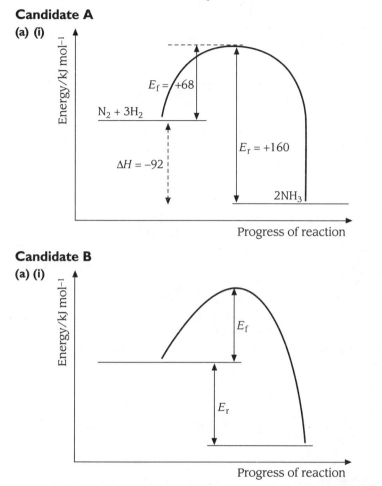

Candidate B

(a) (i)

> The marking points are: products at a lower enthalpy than the reactants ✓; activation energy of forward reaction labelled correctly ✓; activation energy of reverse reaction correctly labelled ✓. Candidate A gives the perfect answer and even goes on to work out ΔH for part (a) (iii). Candidate B scores 1 mark. The enthalpy change for the reverse reaction is incorrect and because the energy levels are not labelled, it is not possible to award the first marking point.

Candidate A

(a) (ii) Activation energy is the minimum energy required to start a reaction.

Candidate B

(a) (ii) It is the energy needed to start the reaction.

> Candidate A gains both marks. Candidate B scores just 1 mark. It is important here to include the key phrase **minimum** energy.

Candidate A

(a) (iii) $-92 \, kJ \, mol^{-1}$

Candidate B

(a) (iii) 92

e Candidate A scores both marks. Candidate B loses a mark because the sign of the enthalpy change for the forward reaction is negative, not positive.

Candidate A

(b) (i) The oxidation state of nitrogen in NH_3 is -3 and in HNO_3 it is $+5$. An increase in oxidation number involves electron loss, which is oxidation (OILRIG).

Candidate B

(b) (i) -3 to $+5$; $N^{-3} \longrightarrow N^{+5} + 8e^{-}$

e Both candidates score full marks. Each candidate has correctly deduced the oxidation numbers and has stated or shown the loss of electrons.

Candidate A

(b) (ii) Le Chatelier's principle states that if a closed system at equilibrium is subject to a change, the system will move to minimise the effect of the change.

Candidate B

(b) (ii) If concentration, temperature and pressure are changed, the system will move to oppose the change. If we increase the concentration, the system moves to decrease the concentration. If we increase the temperature, the system moves to decrease the temperature. If we decrease the pressure, the system tries to move to increase the pressure.

e Both gain 2 marks. Candidate A gives a textbook answer, while Candidate B explains Le Chatelier's principle fully.

Candidate A

(b) (iii) The forward reaction is exothermic and so is favoured by low temperature. There are fewer products than reactants, so high pressure is required.

Candidate B

(b) (iii) Low temperature and high pressure, but in industry a temperature of about 450 °C and a pressure of 200 atm are used.

e Candidate A scores 3 marks. Both conditions are correct and the reason why a low temperature is required is also correct. The final mark is lost because Candidate A does not refer to the relative number of *gas* molecules on each side of the equation. Candidate B gains 2 marks for the correct conditions but scores no marks for the explanation. Candidate B has simply memorised the industrial conditions.

Candidate A

(b) (iv) Reused in stage 2

Candidate B

(b) (iv) Recycled

e Both candidates gain the mark.

Candidate A

(c) An acid is a proton donor. A strong acid dissociates totally into its ions.
$$HNO_3(aq) \longrightarrow H^+(aq) + NO_3^-(aq)$$

Candidate B

(c) $HNO_3(aq) \rightleftharpoons H^+(aq) + NO_3^-(aq)$
An acid is a proton donor and it dissociates totally into its ions.

e Candidate A scores both marks but Candidate B loses a mark. The equation shows the dissociation as reversible, which contradicts the statement that 'it dissociates totally'. Examiners always mark contradictions wrong. They will never select the right answer for you.

Candidate A

(d) $CaCO_3(s) + 2HNO_3(aq) \longrightarrow Ca(NO_3)_2(aq) + H_2O(l) + CO_2(s)$
A gas is given off.

Candidate B

(d) $CaCO_3 + 2HNO_3 \longrightarrow Ca(NO_3)_2 + H_2O + CO_2$
The solid dissolves and it effervesces.

e Candidate A scores 3 marks: 1 mark for the correct equation, 1 for the state symbols and 1 for the evolution of CO_2 gas. Candidate B also scores 3 marks, for a correct equation and two correct observations. The final mark is lost because he/she has failed to include the state symbols.

e This is another good answer from Candidate A, scoring 21 out of 23. This equates to a grade A answer. Candidate B scores 15 of the 23 marks, which is borderline D/C grade. As in previous questions, Candidate B has lost marks carelessly. Look back at B's answers and identify marks that should have been gained. Add these to the total and see the rapid improvement. For this question, 14 marks is approximately a grade C, 16 a grade B and 18 or 19 a grade A. If you can spot the errors in others' work, then it may prevent you from making the same mistakes.

Enthalpy changes using $mc\Delta T$

In an investigation to find the enthalpy change of combustion of ethanol, C_2H_5OH, a student found that 1.60 g of ethanol could heat 150 g of water from 22.0 °C to 71.0 °C. The specific heat capacity of the apparatus was $4.2\,J\,g^{-1}\,K^{-1}$.

(a) Draw a diagram of the apparatus that could be used. (2 marks)

(b) Use the student's results to calculate a value for the enthalpy change of combustion of ethanol. (7 marks)

(c) The theoretical value of the standard enthalpy change of combustion of ethanol is $-1367.3\,kJ\,mol^{-1}$. Give two reasons for the difference in values and suggest an improvement to your apparatus. (3 marks)

(d) Catalysts have great economic importance. Give an example of a catalyst that is in the same state as the reactants and an example of one that is in a different state from the reactants. State why the reaction you have chosen is important and explain how the catalyst is able to increase the rate of reaction. (5 marks)
1 mark is available for the quality of written communication. (1 mark)

Total: 18 marks

Candidates' answers to Question 6

(a) Candidate A   Candidate B

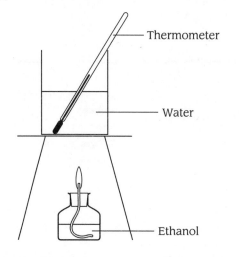

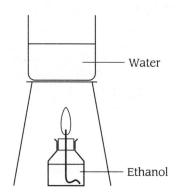

The apparatus required is very simple, but must allow:
- the ethanol to be burnt such that it heats the water
- the increase in temperature to be measured

Candidate A's diagram therefore scores both marks, but Candidate B has lost an easy mark by forgetting to include a thermometer.

Candidate A

(b) $\Delta H = -mc\Delta T$

$\qquad = -(150 \times 4.2 \times 49)$

$\qquad = -30\,870\,J = -30.87\,kJ$

Moles of ethanol $= 1.6/46 = 0.035$

$\Delta H = -30.87/0.035$

$\qquad = -882\,kJ\,mol^{-1}$

Candidate B

(b) $\Delta H = -mc\Delta T = -(1.6 \times 4.2 \times 49) = -329.28\,J$

Moles of ethanol $= 1.6/46 = 0.035$

$\Delta H = -329.28/0.035$

$\qquad = -9408$

🖉 The marking points are: use of the equation $\Delta H = -mc\Delta T$ ✓; mass = 150 ✓; calculates value of ΔH ✓; correct units ✓; moles of ethanol ✓; divides value of ΔH by moles of ethanol ✓; correct units ✓. Candidate A's answer is excellent and scores 7 marks. Candidate B uses an incorrect value for the mass and does not quote any units for the final value, but still scores 5 marks, even though the answer is wrong. This is because all the working is shown and the examiner is able to award marks consequentially by following the initial mistake through the calculation.

Candidate A

(c) Heat is lost to the surroundings. The thermometer is not very accurate. Insulate the beaker to cut down heat losses and avoid draughts.

Candidate B

(c) Heat loss. Incomplete combustion — CO or C may have been formed. Increase the supply of oxygen to ensure that CO_2 is always produced.

🖉 Candidate B gives a very good answer and scores all 3 marks. Candidate A scores 2 marks. Students often criticise apparatus without carefully considering the error. Given that the temperature rise here is approximately 50 °C, even if the thermometer used measured only to the nearest degree, then the percentage error in measuring the temperature rise is of the order $(1/50) \times 100 = 2\%$. Given the inaccuracy of the experiment, this is not of great significance.

Candidate A

(d) Catalysts speed up the rate of reactions and therefore reduce costs. Sulphuric acid is used in the production of esters. The acid is in the same state as the reactants and is known as a homogeneous catalyst. Heterogeneous catalysts, such as Fe, which is used in the Haber process, are catalysts that are in a different state from the reactants. Both types of catalyst work by lowering the activation energy of the reaction.

Candidate B

(d) Esters are made by the reaction between alcohols and carboxylic acids in the presence of an acid catalyst. The acid and the reactants are all liquids and the

6

question

catalyst is a homolytic catalyst. Esters are important as they are used in flavourings. Platinum is used in a catalytic converter to reduce the amount of CO and NO emitted. The platinum is a solid and the reactants are both gases. This is a heterolytic catalyst. Catalysts speed up reactions, without being themselves used up, by providing an alternative route with lower activation energy.

e The marking points are: identification of a suitable example of a homogeneous catalyst ✓; suitable use for product ✓; identification of a suitable example of a hetero-geneous catalyst ✓; suitable use for the product ✓; catalysts lower activation energy ✓. The quality of written communication mark is awarded for appropriate spelling, punctuation, grammar and correct use of at least two of: homogeneous, heterogeneous and activation energy. Candidate A gives a very good answer, but forgets to state a use for each process and therefore loses 2 marks. Candidate A scores a mark for each example, a mark for the explanation of how the catalyst works and gains the mark for quality of written communication. Candidate B scores 5 marks for an example and use of each type of catalyst and a correct explanation of how catalysts work. The mark lost is for quality of written communication — Candidate B has confused homolytic and heterolytic (which refer to bond fission) with homogeneous and heterogeneous (which refer to catalysts).

e **Both candidates do well on this question, with Candidate A scoring 15 out of 18 and Candidate B scoring 14 marks. However, it is still possible to identify where these students have lost marks carelessly. Candidate A drops 2 easy marks in part (d) by not following carefully the instructions in the question. Candidate B loses 2 marks in the calculation in part (b), and also loses a really easy mark in part (a) by not including a thermometer. It is worth remembering that every mark counts. As a rough guide, 80% of the available marks equates to a grade A, 70% of the marks gives a grade B, and 60% equals a grade C. Candidate A scores 15 marks, which gives 83% and hence a grade A, but candidate B, by not including the thermometer, drops to 14 marks or 78% which, if maintained throughout the paper, would give a grade B.**